Louis Falstein

THE MAN WH

The Stor

The Man Who Loved Laughter

OVED LAUGHTER

f Sholom Aleichem

Illustrated by Adrianne Onderdonk Dudden

The Jewish Publication Society of America

Philadelphia • 5728/1968

Contents

1 The comedian

"Up loafers! Time for *cheder!*" Froomeh roused the boys from their heavy sleep. She had a voice of thunder and in her fingers there was the grip of iron. She pushed, shoved and chased the lot of them into the kitchen. Tea was on the table. Butter was thick on the slices of bread. Mother was already gone to open the store in the market place. Father had finished his morning prayers and he too was gone. Froomeh, the one eyed, pock-marked, two-fisted maid saw to it that the half-dozen Rabinowitz boys got off to school without delay.

The boys dressed noisily, if not eagerly.

"Quiet! You'll wake the other children!" Froomeh scolded. "The other children" were the girls and those among the boys too young to attend *cheder.* Altogether there were more than a dozen children, of all sizes, shapes and complexions, black-haired, blond and red-haired. Sholom, known as the middle-one, never bothered counting them all. He knew only that the family was constantly growing larger. There was never a fuss made over the children and it was questionable if any of them would be missed had they not been born. But as they were already on the scene, what harm was there? The children received frequent spankings, particularly from Froomeh and their mother. But when a child took sick, the mother's face became a mask of despair. She clung to the sickbed, muttering: "O woe is me. . . ." The moment the ailing child recovered, the mother underwent a quick transformation. "To *cheder,* loafer!" she cried.

When a child died, the mourning was loud and heartfelt. All the mirrros in the house were covered. The parents took off their shoes and sat on the floor, in the manner of pious Jews, which they were, and wept loudly and bitterly. The week's mourning period over, they rose and returned to their labors.

"Aren't you done eating?" Froomeh pushed them forcibly out of the house. Outside it was still dark. The Rabinowitz boys went wordlessly to *cheder,* grim expressions on their faces, as though they were going to prison. When they arrived, the small, dark room was already filled with boys wearing earlocks and long gabardine coats. The *rebbi* greeted them with: "Congratulations! The Rabinowitz heirs have finally arrived! Just because they happen to be the sons of Reb Nahum, the richest Jew in town, they think they can come in when they *please.*"

Sholom nodded solemnly as the *rebbi* spoke. But as soon as the *rebbi*'s back was turned, the boy began imitating his gestures. The class exploded in laughter. The *rebbi* swung around. "Ah, the comedian has arrived!" he declared, eyeing Sholom meaningfully. He seized the whip, which was never out of reach, and told the comedian to let down his trousers.

Sholom shrugged and obeyed. The whipping he was about to receive was not the first, nor would it be the last. His irresistible impulse to mimic caused him a lot of trouble. He imitated the *rebbi,* his wife, Froomeh—anyone who struck his fancy. In *cheder* he was known as "the comedian." His classmates roared with laughter at his antics.

"Get back to your studies!"

Cheder occupied the whole day. It began with dawn and ended after dark.

Although Sholom spent a good deal of time in his private fantasy world or clowning, he could quote more pages from the Talmud than all his brothers put together. And his handwriting was something to behold. "Extraordinary!" his father said with pride. The wrinkles disappeared from Reb Nahum-Vevik's brow when Sholom displayed his penmanship or recited from the Talmud. Reb Nahum had high hopes for "the comedian," who was his favorite. He urged the boy to study hard. "Do it for me, Sholom, and for yourself."

Reb Nahum was a tall, bearded man, with a large noble brow, always wrinkled. His shoulders were stooped, as though the world's ills were on his back. He was a curious combination: a philosopher and believer in the Haskalah (Enlightenment) who at the same time was a follower of a Chasidic rabbi.

He was very wealthy and also one of the most respected citizens of Voronko. The Rabinowitz house
was where people gathered for important occasions:
to bid farewell to the queen of holidays, the Sabbath; to find out what was happening in the world
outside of Voronko; to drink tea or savor wine; to
read aloud; to discuss the merits of a new rabbi.

Sholom worshiped his father. "I'll study hard," he
promised. But resolve melted as soon as his father
left the room. His mind began to wander. How soon
would he be able to meet his young friend Shmulik?
When would the two of them finally begin to search
for the hidden treasure? Was it advisable to wait
any longer? If they put it off too long, others might
find the treasure. He was impatient for Saturday afternoon when he would be with Shmulik.

In the meantime, he had to put up with *cheder*,
Froomeh and her fists, and the store. The store was
in the market place, where all of the town's busi-
nesses were crowded together. On Fair days the
market place was more crowded than Voronko's Old
Cemetery. To Sholom it seemed the whole world
was on hand, shouting, screaming, bargaining. Peasants came from neighboring villages to sell chickens,
geese and ducks in addition to produce; they took
back with them such items as candles, salt, sugar
and other necessities. On such occasions as Fair
days, Sholom's mother, Haie-Esther, called in her
sons to guard the store against thieves. The boys
responded speedily. When their mother was not
looking, they stuffed their pockets with candies,
nuts, even coins, taken from the cashbox. Sholom

was one of the worst offenders. However, he did not commit the transgressions lightly. He hoped God would not punish him too severely, as he was stealing not only for himself but for Shmulik the Orphan as well. He shared with Shmulik everything he owned: his money and lunches as well as his dreams. He vowed to be with Shmulik forever. What a supply of wonderful tales Shmulik possessed! And how well he told them!

Sholom, breathless with admiration, asked where Shmulik obtained all his stories.

Shmulik, not one to boast, declared he could draw wine from a wall, oil from a ceiling; he could transform sand into gold and make diamonds from broken glass. And all this by means of the Kabala. And Shmulik went on to impart a choice bit of information to his astonished friend. Their rabbi, he told Sholom, was a kabalist. The whole town knew it. At night, when everybody slept, the rabbi busied himself with the Kabala.

Sholom shrugged in disbelief. How did Shmulik know all this?

Shmulik knew! After all, didn't he live in the rabbi's house? An orphan, he shared the rabbi's old dwelling, ate what little food there was on the rabbi's table. No wonder Shmulik was so skinny! But how did he know the rabbi studied the Kabala at night? Did he watch him?

Shmulik protested that he slept at night and could not very well watch the rabbi, but the tiniest baby knew that it was the Kabala that kept the rabbi busy at night. The rabbi could do the impossible! If he wished, the rabbi could open the twelve wells of quicksilver and the thirteen gardens of saffron.

Sholom's astonishment grew. Indeed, their rabbi was an extraordinary person! But he could not help wondering out loud why—in view of all this—Shmulik was always hungry and the rabbi did not have enough money to buy food for the Sabbath.

Shmulik informed his friend that the rabbi preferred it that way. If he wanted to, the rabbi could be richer than anyone, even Rothschild. But he didn't want to be rich. Money meant nothing to him. He'd rather do pennance and suffer.

According to Shmulik, the rabbi knew where the treasure was hidden.

Then why didn't they find out from the rabbi?

"It's not that simple," Shmulik replied.

They sat on top of the hill overlooking Voronko, gazing at the clear afternoon sky. They sat there sniffing the fragrance of the unmown grass. Shmulik talked of the treasure. His eyes took on a dreamy, faraway look, his cheeks caught fire, his imagination soared. It was Bogdan Hmelnitski, he said, who buried the treasure here two centuries ago. He stole and robbed it from the Jews, before he massacred them. Between 1648 and 1658, the cutthroat and his bands killed one hundred thousand Jews. One could well imagine how much he stole from them! And he buried it all on the hill, their hill.

Sholom was on the point of shedding a tear for the loss of it all, but Shmulik consoled him. God didn't create the Kabala for nothing. The kabalists knew how to find the treasure—because they possessed the key words and knew the verse from the Psalms that must be repeated forty times in order for the treasure to reveal itself.

Sholom, more at home with the Psalms than with hidden treasures, demanded to know what verse in the Psalms.

"If I only knew!" Shmulik went on to explain that even if he knew the particular verse, matters would not be solved. It was all very complicated. Not only was it necessary to recite forty chapters from the Psalms, one had to fast forty days, in addition. "You mustn't take the tiniest morsel of food in your mouth during that period." On the forty-first day, immediately after sunset one started stealthily toward the spot where the treasure lay buried. "God help you if anybody sees you!"

"Why?"

"You have to begin all over again."

More than any of Shmulik's fanciful tales, the one about Hmelnitski's treasure made the deepest impression on the future Sholom Aleichem. He was convinced that they would find the treasure. It was only a matter of time. They would find the hoard and divide it equally. He knew exactly what he would do with his share. He would give all the gold to his parents. "Here, use it in the best of health!" He could see the expressions on their faces! No longer would his father have that preoccupied air, his brow wrinkled. As for his mother, there would no longer be any need for her to spend all her waking hours at the store, leaving all the children to the ten-

der mercies of Froomeh, who "educated" them with
her fists.

Even after he had generously disposed of the gold,
there would be sufficient wealth left to build himself
a splendid palace, with an enclosed garden. In the
center of the garden he planned to have a well of
quicksilver. A fierce dog would guard the entrance,
the kind of dog one found among Gentiles, a savage
animal that tore at the long gabardines of Jewish
boys and men. *His* dog would be different; it would
leave Jews alone. And in the midst of all this splendor, he, the prince, would sit enthroned, doling out
alms generously to the poor of Voronko, who were
legion, giving to each according to his needs.

He lived as though in a dream, among princes and
princesses. One day he awakened rudely. The old
rabbi died, and Shmulik the Orphan, his dear friend
Shmulik, whose rich fantasies fired his own imagination and made it soar like the hawks in the clear sky
above Voronko, disappeared. Sholom was irreconcilable. He prayed his friend would return. Had they
not pledged eternal friendship?

He waited, but Shmulik did not come back.
Sholom mourned and remembered. In the vast storehouse that was his mind, where hundreds of names,
places and anecdotes were held against the time
when he would put them on paper, Shmulik the
Orphan remained among the most vivid of his mem-
ories. There were faces, he wrote many years later,
created by God for the purpose of bewitching you at
first glance. His friend, Shmulik, possessed such a
face. And even after half a century had passed, he

called to Shmulik in the pages of his autobiography, *Return From the Fair*. If anyone's heard of Shmulik, he wrote, or knew where he might find him, please respond to his plea. But Shmulik had vanished forever.

Sholom made friends with Meyer. One day he was sitting on top of the hill, near the treasure, where Shmulik had sat with him so often and regaled him with enchanting stories. He sat and sighed, remembering Shmulik and thinking about the treasure.

"Hello."

Startled, Sholom looked up and recognized the new rabbi's son, Meyer Medvedevker.

"What are you doing here?"

Sholom glanced searchingly at the intruder. Does he expect me to tell him I'm guarding our treasure? Sholom thought. "Just sitting," he replied.

"Mind if I join you?"

"I don't own the hill."

Meyer sat down. He put a blade of grass between his lips and regarded Sholom with a grin. "Want to hear me sing?"

"I don't mind."

"I can act too."

"Go ahead, act."

"I expect to be paid," Meyer declared. "I don't perform for nothing. I charge a penny for a song."

"I don't happen to have a penny."

"Then I'll take a pear or a plum or a few raisins. I don't perform for nothing."

Meyer Medvedevker—who many years later became a famous singer—was altogether different from Shmulik. He lacked Shmulik's rich imagination but was gifted with the voice of an angel. When he broke out in song on the street, people stopped to listen. His acting, in Sholom's estimation, was also superb. He taught his new friend to play Robber. He brought along his mother's kitchen knife, tucking it inside his father's broad belt. He marched off, shoeless, followed by his admiring friend, Sholom Rabinowitz, who was forced to play the Jew. "You're the Jew," Meyer declared, "and I'll be the Robber." As a Jew about to be attacked by the cutthroat, Sholom was told by Meyer to find himself a staff and put a pillow inside the back of his jacket to make him look like an unfortunate hunchback. Sholom did as he was told. He became a pitiful figure. Meyer nodded. "Now turn the visor of your cap to one side."

Sholom obeyed. He looked the part, a poor Jewish beggar, walking from town to town, seeking alms. By a stroke of misfortune, the poor beggar got lost in the forest, which was actually Meyer's house. The cutthroat pounced on him crying, "Out with the money!"

Sholom, entering the spirit of the game, importuned the robber to let him go. "Have pity, sir. Have pity on me, on my wife and my children. Don't kill me and make my wife a widow, my children orphans."

"Out with it!" the robber said, gnashing his teeth, waving his menacing knife over the Jew's head. The door opened and the rabbi came in. He seized Meyer, took off his belt and let his son have it!

"Good-for-nothing!" he cried. "Apostate!" Turning to Sholom he said in a voice filled with grievance. "The son of Nahum-Vevik's should not waste his time playing with a no-good like this one!"

Both boys preferred the dusty streets of Voronko to the pages of the Torah. More than learning the Scriptures and the ways of piety, they liked plucking gooseberries or pears from some forbidden fruit tree.

The Talmud, Meyer reasoned, was not a nervous goat about to run away. "The worst that can happen to us, we'll get whipped."

One day Meyer scaled a fence surrounding the priest's orchard. Inside, he quickly filled his pockets with pears. The priest's daughter spied the young intruder, screamed for her father, who came running, followed by a fierce dog. The dog leaped at Meyer, tearing his trousers to shreds.

The whole affair might not have turned out so tragically had it not happened on the Ninth of Ab, the day on which Jews commemorate the destruction of the Temple. Picture to yourself all of Voronko's Jews in their stocking feet, weeping and wailing over the loss of the Temple, and Meyer, son of the rabbi, desecrating the sacred and solemn holiday, racing through the streets without his trousers. In the end, it was the rabbi who paid dearly for Meyer's prank. All the respectable parents of Voronko, Sholom's among them, removed their sons from Meyer's father's *cheder*. The poor man, unable to make a living in town, was forced to leave.

Sholom then became friends with Gergele the Thief. Gergele taught him how to commit many transgressions.

"Can't you find another friend?" Sholom's parents scolded.

"Can't you find a decent boy for a friend?" Grandma Mindy demanded.

It was freely predicted that Sholom would come to no good end. It was not only his parents and Grandma Mindy who lectured him and prophesied his doom; all the grownups in the world seemed ranged against him, scolding and reprimanding. He saw fingers shaking at him everywhere. His ears buzzed with warnings:

"Don't play with this one!"

"Stay away from that one!"

"Don't sit here!"

"Don't stand there!"

A torrent of words assailed him: from his father, mother, brothers, sisters, the *rebbi,* Froomeh, uncles aunts, Grandma—particularly Grandma.

Grandma Mindy was a tall, well-groomed woman, and extremely pious. It was her duty, she declared, to keep a sharp eye on the children's religious up-bringing. She made certain, for one thing, that they knew and said their prayers. Every Sabbath after-noon, after prayers, she summoned all the grand-children, ordered them to sit quietly while she treated them to apples, pears and raisins, scolding them all the while, warning them to obey their par-ents and all pious Jews, to be good Jews themselves. God would punish, Grandma Mindy warned, for the tiniest sin, for not praying, not obeying, not studying and—gazing at Sholom meaningfully—for being a comedian.

Grandma Mindy's lectures were a heavy yoke, but they were nothing as compared with the *rebbi's* in *cheder.* He drew rivers of tears from the students, so sharp and bold were his descriptions of the suffering awaiting them in hell. The *rebbi* made them tremble with fear. No child in the room, he cried, was immune. They were all sinners, all candidates for the fires of Gehenna. Even if among them was one who did not sin, who said his prayers regularly and studied diligently, he too was guilty, with the rest, for being tempted by the Evil Spirit.

There was no escaping the clutches of the Evil Spirit! Sholom tried hard. But he was fighting a losing battle. Could he help it if laughter came to his lips when solemnity was required? He was powerless when a joke begged to be told, when he hurried with his prayer, skipping a line here and there because the sun shone brightly outside and he was eager to play. He was powerless against forbidden thoughts that sometimes crept into his mind. Much as he was tempted by the Evil Spirit. Sholom nevertheless thought of himself as a pious boy. He feared God and swore that when he grew up he would mend his ways and be good, as Grandma Mindy desired, as the *rebbi* ordered. For the time being, however, he could not resist Gergele the Thief—and Seerko, the dog.

Seerko was an ordinary dog, yet he was not ordinary. He never bit Jews, a claim no other dog in town would care to make. Seerko eagerly responded when his master, Sholom, ordered him to sit up, lie down, or stand on his two hind legs. Master and slave spent many hours together behind the garbage pile in the courtyard. Sholom would have liked to bring his dog inside the house, but this was forbidden. Once Sholom invited Seerko into their kitchen. Froomeh flew into a rage and poured scalding water on the poor dog, leaving a mark on its hide that Seerko carried the rest of his life.

"I'll have no animals inside this house!" Froomeh screamed.

Sholom retreated, vanquished. He recalled with a shudder how Froomeh treated a stray cat that dared set its foot in the kitchen not long ago. Seizing the cat, Froomeh tied it to the foot of the table, grabbed a broomstick and flailed away.

Sholom, tears in his eyes, pleaded with her to let the poor cat go, to beat him instead—but to no avail.

He could not stand cruelty to animals. A dog with a broken leg brought tears to his eyes. He loved cats and shielded them from the wrath of grownups. His love of animals brought him many troubles. What did a Jewish boy want with animals? Goats, yes. Goats provided a family's milk supply. Goats were kept inside homes, often sleeping with the rest of the family in the only bedroom. But cats and dogs were luxuries most Jewish families could not afford. Often there was not enough food for the children, let alone pets! Gentiles owned dogs to guard their property against thieves. Most Jews were too poor to own property and had nothing of value to guard. They were on uneasy terms with domestic animals such as dogs and cats. The children were taught early to fear and mistrust them.

Sholom did not heed the warnings. They would not separate him from Seerko! When sadness crept over him, following a scolding at home or in *cheder,* he sought out Seerko. The two of them took refuge at the far end of the courtyard, behind the garbage pile. He recalled Ecclesiastes and King Solomon's words: *A man has no preeminence over a beast.* He stroked Seerko's fur lovingly and hugged the dog, murmuring, "Dear friend, Seerko."

In late summer the heat held Voronko in its grip. Not a drop of rain fell to cool the parched little town. Rumor spread like a forest fire that a dog had gone mad from the heat, biting several other dogs. Panic seized the Jews of Voronko. The Rabinowitz children were all rounded up by Froomeh and taken to old Trofim, a peasant known in town as a conjuror. So skillful was Trofim, so dexterous with his hands, a child scarcely felt any pain. Returning home, the Rabinowitz children were told to stay indoors. Froomeh locked them inside. She kept them under lock and key until the dogs of Voronko, Seerko among them, had been rounded up and taken away.

Sholom refused to eat. At night he closed his eyes but could not sleep.

2 From riches to rags

For the boy Sholom, Voronko was the center of the universe and its Jews the select of God. There was not a town more lively or exciting. There was magic even in the name: Voronko!

It mattered not at all to him that this cramped little community, tucked away on several piddling acres in the Poltava region of the Ukraine, was congested and dirty, the people living like herring in a barrel. Part of the Pale of Settlement, an area where Jews were permitted to reside, the town had fewer residents than a fair-sized housing project in an American city. After a rain the roads were impassable piles of mud. The people lived in wooden shacks—all but the few who were wealthy—with thatched roofs over their heads and mud floors under their feet. Sewers were unknown. The market place, where the Rabinowitz store was located, was the center of the town. The most crowded place was the Old Cemetery, many of whose tenants had been there long before Columbus sailed to discover America.

With very few exceptions people spoke Yiddish, the "mother tongue." The men wore beards and all males had earlocks curling under their broad-brimmed hats. The women put on wigs soon after marriage.

The Sabbath was a day of rest and renewal. Hordes of beggars marched from house to house, from town to town. This was Voronko when Sholom was a boy. He loved it with all his heart.

It did not occur to him that one day he would be torn from his beloved Voronko and taken to a strange and hostile place where not a soul knew him for what he was: Reb Nahum-Vervik's son. And yet, it happened—not long after Seerko vanished. At home, where for years he'd considered his father's position as impregnable, Sholom heard strange and baffling talk: Voronko, his parents whispered, was not the *only* place in the world; one could make a living elsewhere as well.

What were the grownups talking about? Why the secretive whispers?

Sholom asked questions but received no answers. He persisted and finally found out that his father no longer possessed his business. How was that possible? Sholom wondered. Wasn't his father one of the most powerful men in town?

"You father was cheated out of his business," Sholom was finally told. "His partner stole from him. Now he has nothing."

Sholom was flabbergasted. He heard his uncles

and aunts urging his father, "Prosecute the crook! Take him to court!"

"I'll not drag a Jewish name through a Christian court," Reb Nahum said. Rather than do that, he decided to take his family and move to another town. There's an old saying: Change your place of habitation and your luck changes too.

His father's words stunned Sholom. He was less concerned with the loss of their livelihood than with having to part with Voronko. They could not expect him to part with the town. And the treasure! He had heard from his friend Pinele that there were cities and towns beyond the rim of the hill more beautiful than Voronko. Sholom doubted it. Voronko held everything he desired.

Pinele laughed. "You should see Pereyaslav! *That's* a city. It even has sidewalks."

"What are those?"

"To walk on, instead of the mud."

In Pereyaslav, according to Pinele, dwellings rose to a dizzy height of three stories. And their sidewalks didn't disappear each time it rained because they were made of wood.

Sholom was skeptical. It didn't seem possible. Where did they acquire so much wood?

But Pinele knew! He had been there—for his operation to remove a pea.

The incident with the pea which led to Pinele's discovery of the world outside of Voronko began this way: Pinele, who had an inquisitive mind, tried an experiment. He put a hard pea in one ear, bent over and waited for it to emerge from the other. The stubborn pea refused to budge. Instead, it began to swell. It gave Pinele such a headache he confessed the whole truth to his mother, who gave him a whipping. Pins were stuck in his ears, wires and all sorts of sharp objects. In the end it was necessary to take him to the large city of Pereyaslav for the "operation." When he came back to Voronko, Pinele was filled with tales about the great world beyond the horizon.

Sholom found his friend's words disquieting. He was eager to stay in Voronko. Even without Shmulik, Meyer and Seerko, Voronko was still the most wonderful place in the world. But he was powerless against the mysterious forces operating the world of grownups. His father appeared determined to move, his mother agreed. The date was set, the packing began.

For Sholom and those of his brothers who attended *cheder,* there was a temporary reprieve. "I don't want to interrupt your studies," Reb Nahum-Vevik's said to the boys as the packing began, "so I arranged for you to stay in Voronko till the end of the term."

The delay gave Sholom what little consolation he could derive from the whole affair.

On the day of his parents' departure all of Voronko turned out. Tears flowed in torrents. The coachman sat impatiently on top of the open wagon, his whip in one hand and the reins in the other, waiting to start. While all the grownups acted as though it were the Ninth of Ab, sobbing and sighing, Sholom and his brothers were in a jubilant mood. Soon the parents would be gone, taking the small children with them, and they, the big ones, would remain. The tumult, the noise, the lip-smacking, made Sholom feel as though he were at a party. There was an additional reason for celebration: no *cheder*.

At the end of the summer, the *cheder* term coming to a close, the inevitable happened. A coachman with three horses attached to his dray arrived from Pereyaslav. "I have a letter from your father," he said to the Rabinowitz boys.

They eagerly opened the letter and read it. "Come immediately," Reb Nahum wrote, "with the bearer of this letter." Sholom, who had expected his father to write at greater length, was disappointed. Why such a short, curt note? Why didn't his father write about their new home in Pereyaslav and about his business? No doubt his father was doing well in the large city. He felt confident his father was wealthy again; he could not conceive of his father as being poor. But why was he so secretive?

For Sholom the most painful moment of all, the leave-taking, began. In his eyes Voronko was suddenly transformed into a living thing, a dear, beloved friend from whom parting was filled with sorrow. He started his farewells in the courtyard with a nod at the garbage pile. In the orchard he took leave of the stately trees, trees he no longer considered his own. He ran to the hill beyond the synagogue, and the meadow outside the town, places he'd come to consider as part of himself. Standing there briefly,

lost in thought, he heard the clear sharp voices of his
friends, Shmulik, Meyer and the rest. He climbed to
the top of the hill, where the treasure was hidden.
Disturbing thoughts assailed his mind. What if a
Gentile some day found the treasure, instead of a
Jew? No, this was not possible. Only Shmulik knew
how to go about finding it! Where was Shmulik
now? Some day they would meet, clasp hands and
return to Voronko and revisit all the lovely places of
their boyhood. And they would go to work in ear-
nest with the forty days of fasting and the recital of
forty chapters from the Psalms. Finally they would
lay their hands on the treasure. He would not keep
anything of his share; he would give all of it to his
father and the poor Jews of Voronko.

Several hours later they left.

After two days of travel over gutted roads, they
arrived at their destination, hungry, sleepy, their
bones aching. It was evening. The three weary
horses entered a dark courtyard and stopped. The
coachman told them to get out. They had arrived at
their destination.

"This?" Sholom said. It could not be! He saw a
large, rambling, run-down house, in need of repair.
A smoky lantern hung over the door of the house.
Underneath the lantern was a bundle of straw. "But
this is an inn," Sholom cried, unable to conceal his
disappointment, "a broken-down old inn."

"Your father's," the coachman said, helping down
the smaller boys.

Crestfallen, Sholom started toward the house. He

recalled his father's oft-repeated words: Change your place of habitation and you change your luck. His father's luck had changed, he thought, for the worse.

"Come on," the coachman prodded, "don't you want to go in and see your parents?"

Sholom started. "I'm coming."

In the distance, under a flickering light, he saw several figures. A short, slight one, his mother; a tall, stooping one, his father. The medium-sized one was Grandma Mindy.

The two groups ran to meet each other. There were embraces, tears and loud exclamations. "Sholom Aleichem! [Greetings!]."

Sholom was aware, even as they were led noisily inside the house, that their lives had been transformed, irrevocably, for the worse. In his father's manner there was constraint; his mother appeared distraught.

"Are you hungry?"

Of course they were hungry! Sholom examined the inside of the inn. Where were the guests? He did not see any. In every room he saw cots, but not one solitary guest. His heart sank. An inn without guests. His father must be poor. The buried treasure came to mind. If he could lay his hands on at least one precious stone of Bogdan Hmelnitksi's hoard! He would offer the diamond to his father and tell him to buy some kerosene for the lamps to brighten the rooms and get new furniture. The furniture, he saw, belonged to their Voronko days; it was now old, chipped, inadequate. It was necessary to fix up the outside too. The place looked run down. Better still, give up the inn and go back to Voronko.

They were called to eat.

Sholom took note of the warmed-over gruel and stale bread. He watched his mother cut the bread instead of letting the boys slice their own. After they'd finished eating, she locked the bread in the cupboard. Sholom exchanged meaningful glances with one of his brothers, as if to say: "Things are bad. In Voronko she never locked the bread in the cupboard."

Reb Nahum summoned the boys. "I want to hear what you've learned this summer," he said. "Who wants to be the first?"

As the boys began their recital, led as usual by Sholom, though he was not the oldest, Reb Nahum's face brightened, the wrinkles on his forehead vanished. "Very good," he said, pleased, "very good."

To Sholom it seemed that for the moment, at least, his father was oblivious of the burdens imposed by his life in Pereyaslav.

They were put to sleep on the floor. Sholom could not sleep. He lay wide awake, sobbing. If only he could do something, for his parents, for himself! But what could a small boy wearing earlocks and a long gabardine coat do in a strange, large, hostile city?

The boys were awakened early. Sholom washed quickly and recited the morning prayers. He prayed with feeling, enunciating each word clearly. God must hear him and help him!

After breakfast he peeked outside. He did not expect to see anything of interest. He glanced suspiciously at the street. Structures rising three stories high flung themselves audaciously at the sky. He had never seen anything like it! And the streets were like broad parade grounds! The wooden sidewalks stretched for miles. It took your breath away.

3 Bible boy

Sholom's fame as a student of the Bible preceded him to Pereyaslav. His father, who had very little in which to take pride, was responsible for trumpeting Sholom's achievements. It was not suprising, therefore, that Aunt Hannah, on making the boy's acquaintance, said to him: "Come here, Bible boy, and say hello to your aunt."

Aunt Hannah was a well-to-do widow. She had a magnificent home, with fruit in large crystal bowls and candy in many colorful little dishes. Compared to the inn, her place was a palace.

In her imperious voice, Aunt Hannah ordered that the Bible boy be given tea, an apple and a pear. After he has finished eating, she said, they would call Ali and Avreml to test Sholom to see how much Torah and Talmud he *really* knew. She smiled as she said this and there was a twinkle in her eye.

Sholom agreed to submit to a test. How could one possibly refuse so grand a lady as Aunt Hannah?

Ali and Avreml were summoned. They were no longer boys. Both of them sported young beards which made them appear in Sholom's eyes like a pair of goats.

"Give him a test," Aunt Hannah said.

"Gladly," the two said in unison. They looked at the little stranger with blond earlocks and a long gabardine coat. They exchanged meaningful glances, as if to say, "We'll dispose of *him* in a hurry!" They began hurling questions at Sholom, about the Torah, Talmud and Rashi's commentaries. Sholom gave rapid-fire answers. Reb Nahum grinned; he seemed to expand with pride.

Aunt Hannah applauded. Beaming at Sholom, she ordered that he be given another apple, pear, several walnuts and all the candy he could eat.

Word spread in Pereyaslav about Sholom's feats of learning. Strangers stopped him in the street, seized him affectionately by the ear and inquired where they might find this or that quotation.

Sholom would tell them, without any hesitation.

The only person in Pereyaslav who seemed unimpressed was Uncle Pinney. In Uncle Pinney's house, one of the most pious in town, the study of the Bible was said to be a pastime for freethinkers. But penmanship was held in high esteem.

"Then why don't you test his handwriting?" Reb Nahum said to his brother. If Pinney, the stubborn one, refused to be impressed by Sholom's phenominal memory, he would surely come around when he saw the boy's exquisite penmanship.

"I will," Uncle Pinney said, and requested a pen and some paper.

There being no paper in the house, a book was given the boy. Sholom's father told him to start writing.

He shrugged. He didn't know what to write. He dipped the pen in a bottle of ink and held it poised over the naked page. His mind was a blank. Uncle Pinney and his two boys were hovering nearby. He thought he heard them snicker.

Sholom wrote what came to mind: "I am writing in this book. Why am I writing in this book? Because I am writing in this book."

And he went on and on in this fashion, covering the whole page, while Uncle Pinney gaped, momentarily at a loss for words.

Sholom's all-around scholarship also proved of practical value. It helped his brother Hershel secure a bride.

Hershel was a handsome youth, with blond curly hair like Sholom's, but without his younger brother's talent for study. As he was Reb Nahum Rabinowitz's son, professional matchmakers came often to the inn with offers of good marriages. One matchmaker, eager to earn a large commission, brought the Rabinowitzes together with a wealthy Jew from Vasilkov who had a marriageable daughter. The Vasilkov man wrote Reb Nahum that he was coming to Pereyaslav to look over the prospective groom.

Reb Nahum wrote in reply: "You will be welcomed like royalty."

As was the custom among Jews in those days, the man from Vasilkov brought with him a person versed in the Bible as well as Hebrew and grammar. He intended thoroughly to examine and test the young man who aspired to be his son-in-law.

At home there were some doubts whether Hershel could pass an examination. However, for Hershel to fail was out of the question! They could not afford it. The girl, whom none of them had met, would bring with her a substantial dowry. Hershel must not fail!

A tutor was hired to coach him. Hershel tried hard.

The day of the encounter drew near. One morning the Vasilkov man made his appearance. With him was a young man in his twenties. "This is my expert," the man from Vasilkov said. "If *he* says your son knows his lessons, there'll be a wedding."

Reb Nahum made the introductions. He presented the members of the family and Hershel's tutor, who stood by nervously, pulling at his white beard.

The young expert from Vasilkov, who was something of a show-off, said to the old tutor, "Can I ask you a few questions?" Before the tutor had time to reply, the other was at him, hurling questions like poisoned arrows. The old man, bewildered by the assault, replied as best he could. "If this executioner gets his claws into Hershel," the flustered tutor said to the Rabinowitz clan later, "our groom is lost. He'll never pass."

Something had to be done, a plan devised, or the desirable match would be off. But obviously nobody could perform the miracle of making Hershel into a

Bible boy like his younger brother, Sholom. The cause seemed lost. And all the delicacies prepared by Haie-Esther were a waste of money and energy.

Suddenly the tutor's glance fell on little Sholom, who hovered in the background, eyeing the festive table hungrily, wondering how he could get his hands on some of the food.

"Come with me," the tutor said to Sholom. They left the room and came back almost instantly. Sholom disappeared behind the couch. The tutor seized Hershel by the arm and said, "You sit on the couch, right here."

"Are we ready?" the Vasilkov "expert" asked, entering the room.

"Ready," Hershel's tutor said with a stammer.

The young man rubbed the palms of his hands and eyed Hershel greedily as though he intended to eat him. He sat in a chair several feet removed from the prospective bridegroom and fired the first question, which sounded to Hershel like a bewildering jumble of words about someone slipping with his feet and being as a lamp despised in thought of him who is at ease.

But Sholom knew instantly it was from the Book of Job and whispered the information to Hershel, who stated it loudly.

"That's right," the torturer conceded. He next demanded that Hershel tell him of another word in the Bible with the same root as *ashtut* [thoughts].

"In Psalms," Sholom whispered to his brother.

The examiner nodded, declaring they were done

with the Bible. He cast a longing glance at the festive table where Haie-Esther was puttering as if she had no doubt about the outcome of the test. "Let's try grammar," he said, ordering Hershel to conjugate the verb "to perish," in Hebrew.

Sholom prompted and his brother echoed the reply.

The examiner raised a hand and cried, "That'll do!" He turned to the prospective father-in-law and declared that the young man obviously knew his way around. "Congratulations!" In the next instant he was stuffing his mouth with delicacies.

Many years later, Sholom Aleichem, writing about the incident, wondered whether the parents were aware of the tutor's ruse. Perhaps this was a plot between the tutor, his brother and himself. Another possibility: the examiner himself may have been aware of what was happening. However, the important thing was the result, and this was pleasing to both sides. Hershel and his bride were happy.

After the marriage, the Bible boy resumed his studies. But these were interrupted when tragedy struck the family.

4 Death in the family

Epidemics were frequent occurrences in Eastern
Europe when Sholom Aleichem was a child. The
unsanitary conditions made the crowded small
towns particularly vulnerable. Thousands of people
died. After each holocaust, the survivors took up
where they had left off.

The cholera epidemic struck Pereyaslav in the
early summer. Terror spread through the town and
the region. The children were kept home from
school. Volunteer brigades were formed to massage
the bodies of the sick, such exercise being considered helpful. Among the volunteers were the most
respectable men in town. They were highly regarded
and readily welcomed in the homes. Sholom's father
volunteered, responding to calls by day or night. He
hardly slept. His wife, uneasy from the start, complained that he might bring the disease into the
house.

Reb Nahum replied calmly that cholera was not

the kind of sickness one brought home. Whoever was fated, would get it.

Several days later, Haie-Esther complained of a burning fever. She took to bed. After a short illness she died.

Sholom was grief-stricken. He felt keenly the loss of his mother. She had not been the most considerate and patient of mothers, he later wrote; she had, in fact, been quick with her temper and her hands. When they had been well, she cursed them, but as soon as one of them took ill, she invoked all the plagues upon herself, tearfully asking God to spare the child.

The family sat on the floor in their stocking feet, observing the ritual of *shiveh,* mourning the dead.

If I had the treasure now, Sholom mused, sitting near his father, it surely would come in handy! He would give it to his father and maybe he would stop groaning and saying life was worthless because Mother was dead. His mind soared away, out of the crowded, stifling room. Treasure, treasure. . . . His father's groans tore him back to reality, back to the dismal world of sighs, groans and tears.

Uncle Pinney announced it was time for the evening prayer. At the appropriate moment in the service, all those mourning, among them the six Rabinowitz sons, rose and began reciting *Kaddish.*

A distant relative, hearing the boys, observed that their mother would surely go to heaven with such *Kaddish* readers!

His mother's death was a severe blow, but there was no denying that being an orphan had certain advantages. Grownups called him "poor orphan." Grandma Mindy referred to the children lovingly as "unfortunate worms." People stopped and stroked his head. It seemed to Sholom he was being noticed for the first time in his life. Visitors asked him how he felt. Women put their palms to his forehead and inquired about his health and his stomach. He had never known he possessed a stomach. Now even strangers inquired about it. It was a pleasure, the fuss people made over you! Moreover, no school. This alone made it a grand holiday. On the table there were white twist breads served with sweet tea.

And what Sholom liked best of all was sitting on the floor near his father and observing the crowds of men and women going in and out, without a how-do-you-do or a goodbye. He realized later that this was the way in which grownups behaved when someone died, leaving out all salutations. But at the time he found it very strange and confusing. The actions of the grownups made him want to laugh and weep at the same time.

Take Uncle Pinney as an instance. Uncle Pinney arrives with his two sons, Isrolik and Itzl, both boys dressed in long coats. Uncle Pinney rolls up his sleeves and begins to talk, while his two boys stand like ramrods, holding their tongues. He wants to know when they are to end the seven days of mourning, in the morning or in the evening? He puckers his mouth, sits down, rises, and declares he will have to consult a couple of books on this point of Law. He nods to his two sons and all three of them leave without saying goodbye.

No sooner is Uncle Pinney gone than Aunt Hannah arrives with her daughters. She enters without saying hello and begins to take Reb Nahum to task. She wants the sobbing to end. Haie-Esther will not be brought back to life with their tears! Aunt Hannah stays awhile, asks the children how they feel, how are their stomachs? She gets up, takes out a silver snuffbox, treats herself to a pinch of snuff and leaves without a farewell.

Reb Nahum's groans continued into the seventh day. Finally, Uncle Pinney said it was time to stop.

But Reb Nahum was irreconcilable. What would he do with the children? What would happen to the children?

Uncle Pinney, always ready with advice, suggested to his brother that the older ones go back to *cheder,* right away, and the younger ones be sent away to their grandparents in Boguslav.

But Reb Nahum said he could not do it.

Uncle Pinney said there was nothing else he *could* do.

Sholom, who had been listening—though the conversation was not meant for his ears—ran to tell his brothers and informed them there was a trip to Boguslav in the offing.

"For whom?"

"The younger ones," he replied.

"Why can't we all go?"

All of them were eager to make the journey to faraway Boguslav where their maternal grandparents lived. Grandfather Moishe-Yossi and Grandma Gittl were said to be wealthy.

Sholom wondered if he would be among those chosen to go. Although a bar-mitzvah boy and treated with respect in the synagogue, as was his due, Sholom was among the half dozen younger children. This entitled him to make the journey.

Reb Nahum was noncommital. Six would go, he said, and six would stay.

"What about me?" Sholom asked.

"We'll see."

He lived in a state of uncertainty. The High Holy Days were drawing near. Reb Nahum summoned all his children and told them he had hired a horse and wagon and several of them were going away to visit their grandparents. He selected two girls and four boys. Sholom was delighted to be among those chosen.

Boguslav was a great distance away. To get to it, they rode several days and crossed the great Dnieper River on a ferryboat. Sholom relished the adventure. He fancied himself an explorer journeying to distant lands, crossing treacherous rivers, storming the gates of fabulous cities.

They arrived on the fourth day. Sholom's heart beat wildly as the coachman drove along the city's narrow streets. He looked at the houses on both sides of the street, wondering which palatial home was his grandfather's. The coachman continued cracking the whip over his horses. They left the neighborhood of the well-appointed homes. Soon they were in a street of ramshackle dwellings, where poor Jews lived.

"Here we are."

They halted in front of a small frame house, so old it was settling.

"Out you go."

The six bewildered children were led past a creaking porch and shown the door. The coachman said, "Go in."

Sholom hesitated and pushed the rickety door. He saw a dark, dismal room in the middle of which stood a wooden bed. On the bed he saw an old woman with twisted limbs. She looked more dead than alive. Sholom, his hand on the doorknob, retreated. It must be a mistake, he thought.

"Wait."

"I—I—" Sholom stammered, coloring.

"What do you want?" the old woman asked, eyeing the cluster of children, the youngest no more than a year old.

Sholom, the spokesman, said they had just arrived from Pereyaslav.

"Say that again," she demanded, stiffening.

Sholom repeated the word "Pereyaslav."

The old woman let out a wail, raised her arms and began raining blows on her head. She summoned her husband, Moishe-Yossi, screaming: "Our daughter is dead!"

A little door opened at the side of the room. An

old ragged man emerged, a prayer shawl draped over his rags.

"Haie-Esther is dead," the old woman sobbed. "Here are her poor orphans."

Grandfather Moishe-Yossi threw the children a withering look. He called them criminals, murderers, in Hebrew, as it was unseemly to carry on in any other language during prayers—which had been so rudely interrupted. Why didn't they come to him first? he scolded them. He would have told her in his own way, so as not to upset her, he said, pointing to Grandma Gittl.

Grandma Gittl, momentarily forgetting her woes, told her husband to leave the children alone. Why pick on them? She wiped her eyes with the crook of her arm, asked the children to approach her bed and tell her their names.

The children came toward her in single file and whispered their names. She kissed each one of them and swore she had known all along her Haie-Esther was dead. She had come to her in her dreams, poor Haie-Esther. She ceased sobbing, ran the crook of her arm over her face to wipe away the tears. Then she told her husband the children must be starved, they needed something to eat. "Feed them," she sighed. "Such a—a fine reception this turned out to be!"

Sholom's "rich" grandfather spent most of his waking hours in prayer. He shouted at the children, in Hebrew, for disturbing his prayers. Grandpa, who was a Chasid and kabalist, was rarely without his

prayer shawl and phylacteries. Sholom found the old
man once cooped up in his little, dark, stifling
chamber, muttering his prayers, his eyes half shut,
as though in a trance. Then he seemed suddenly to
come awake with a start. His eyes brightened, a
smile was on his lips and he said out loud that
Edom's rule was coming to an end. . . . Salvation was
at hand. He spied Sholom and asked him in a soft
voice to come and sit with him and hear about the
Messiah. . . .

He embraced the boy. He told him of the wonderful things that would come to pass when the Messiah came to free the Jews from their long exile and
return with them triumphantly to the Land of Israel.
Grandpa's eyes shone as he spoke. Each one of his
words was a bird taking wing. Sholom listened, en-
raptured. Shmulik came to mind, his first and dearest friend. Like Shmulik, Grandpa Moishe-Yossi
painted his word pictures with flaming colors. The
difference between the two was that Shmulik used to
concern himself with buried treasures, sorcerers,
princes and princesses, aspects of *this* world,
whereas Grandpa Moishe-Yossi made short shrift of
this world. The old man took flight in the next world,
where angels, saints, seraphim and cherubim
crowded near God's throne. Suddenly the grandfather broke out in song. His eyes were raised toward heaven. His face was aglow with ecstasy. To
Sholom, who watched in fascination, Grandpa already seemed far away, in another world.

Of all the orphans the grandfather liked Sholom
best, even though he considered him a mischief-

maker and a loafer who wasted his time watching the fishermen on the wharf, and playing with no-goods. He said the boy had a good head on his shoulders, he could make something of him, if Sholom's father left him there, in Boguslav, for a few years. He could make a real pious Jew of Sholom, a Chasid, a kabalist. But if he went back to Pereyaslav, he would be a nobody, a loafer, a dumbell.

During the High Holy Days, Grandfather Moishe-Yossi detached himself completely from the family and the brood of young visitors. He seemed to be in a world of his own, one of religious fervor and ecstasy. He arrived at the synagogue before anyone else and remained there at night, long after the others had gone home. On Simchas Torah, the Feast of the Rejoicing in the Law, Grandpa rose early. He drank a glass of whiskey, in honor of the holiday, and a half glass of wine. He emerged on the street and went into a dance. Sholom, who followed the old man, stopped to watch in amazement. He had never seen such nimble dancing! The old man whirled, bounced and flung himself in the air. He clapped his hands, raised his head toward the sky and shouted God's praises.

After the holidays Sholom began to miss his father and Pereyaslav. Long stretches of time passed between letters. The boy worried about his father and how things were going at the inn. The pleasure of not having to go to *cheder* had worn off some time ago.

The cool weather arrived before they were sum-

moned home. Several days after Sholom's return to
Pereyaslav, his father disappeared. Sholom, concerned, made inquiries.

"Your father had to go to Berdichev," Grandma
Mindy said.

"What for?"

"To find himself a wife."

"A wife?"

"A wife. What else?"

Sholom impatiently waited for his father's return.
What kind of wife would he bring back? He could
not help feeling occasional resentment against his father for marrying so soon after his mother's death.
However, the boy was aware that good Jews were
duty-bound to marry. He recalled the exchange between his father and Uncle Pinney the day after his
mother's funeral. When the former lamented that all
was lost, his end had come, the latter countered that
he was talking nonsense, that after a decent interval
he would find himself another wife.

Now his father was only doing what was expected
of him.

Letters began arriving from Berdichev. Finally
Reb Nahum wrote: "I have found her."

The boys wrote back: "Congratulations!" They
expected the arrival of their father and his bride at
any moment.

Reb Nahum appeared in no hurry to come back to
Pereyaslav. Instead, he informed the family: "I am
getting married in Berdichev."

Several days later, he brought her home to Pereyaslav. The older boys were in *cheder* when a mes-

senger came in, summoning them home. The boys ran all the way, eager to have a look at their stepmother.

They found a houseful of people: Uncle Pinney and his sons, Aunt Hannah and her daughters. They were seated around the table, drinking tea and eating cakes. Sholom's eyes sought out the stepmother in the crowd. He was surprised to find she possessed no horns, as one expected of a stepmother. Quite the contrary, she appeared friendly and sociable. During the introductions she smiled and shook the boys' hands and even inquired about their work in *cheder*. Sholom, observing her from a distance, approved of his father's choice. They were all fortunate! Stepmothers, every one knew, were more cruel than the winter winds blowing from Siberia. This one would be different. He sighed with relief and reached for a cake offered him.

The last guest having departed, the door closed, their new mother turned a cold stare on Reb Nahum. "How many children did you say you had?" she demanded.

"Why—eh—" Reb Nahum stammered, caught off guard.

"In Berdichev you told me you had six," she said with asperity. "Here I find twice as many!"

Poor Reb Nahum! He had been so eager to find a new mother for his children, he told her of six children in Pereyaslav, failing to mention he had six more in Boguslav. He paid dearly for this little oversight, and the children did too.

The stepmother had an explosive temper. Each one of her sentences was accompanied by a curse. Often she cursed in rhymes. Sholom, fascinated by her colorful expressions, wrote them down. It did not occur to him that as a writer he would some day make use of the material. In the end he accumulated a fat volume. He called it "Stepmother's Vocabulary." It was his first written work. It was almost his last too, as his stepmother found the notebook and read it from beginning to end. She then proceeded to find ways of making his life intolerable.

5 The Jewish Robinson Crusoe

At the Rabinowitz inn business was poor. Most of the rooms and the cots in them were empty. On occasion a traveler stopped, a wheat merchant passing through, or a man dealing in animal skins. Then the hissing, boiling samovar was placed in the center of the large table and Sholom's father sat at the head, wearing a skullcap, listening with one ear to the tales of his guest and with the other to his wife abusing the children. He frowned and looked away. She abused his children often. He kept silent.

The boys went to *cheder* half of the day. The other half they spent at home, helping with the work at the inn, cleaning, scrubbing, caring for the step-mother's little children. Sholom was exiled to a place near the road. "When you see a passing coach," the stepmother instructed him, "with passengers inside, tell them to stop here."

"How should I tell them?" Sholom asked sheepishly.

"With your tongue," replied the harassed woman. "Tell them this is the best inn in town. Our samovar is always boiling. Our beds are clean. And we are cheaper than—"

"I'll do the best I can," the boy promised.

"You *better*—if you want to eat."

Working outside had certain advantages; one was away from the stepmother's sharp barbs and prying eyes. He found a little old stool and placed it near the gate and sat down. "Here! Stop here!" he cried, sighting a carriage filled with strangers.

In response to Sholom's invitation, the coachman raised his whip and cracked it and there was an explosion in the air. In an instant the coach disappeared, leaving Sholom enveloped in a cloud of dust.

The boy sighed. He saw visions of going to bed without food.

He sat on the stool in front of the gate during the hot summer months when the air was so calm one could not breathe. It was worse in the winter when the numbing frost penetrated his torn garments and worn boots.

"Here! Stop here!" he shouted at the passing coaches. The horses sped by, ignoring his plea. He followed them with his eyes filled with tears. He knew without a shred of doubt that all the coaches that passed would stop down the road, at the Yasnegradski inn.

Like a powerful magnet Yasnegradski drew them

all! Yasnegradski gave them large rooms, soft beds, unblemished mirrors. How unlike his father's inn, empty as a desert!

Why didn't God make him the son of Yasnegradski?

In his mind's eye, Yasnegradski stood for wealth and happiness. Only rich guests stopped there! They came in large coaches, drawn by swift horses. They clambered down, puffing from the effort, their fat bodies wrapped in expensive bearskins. In his reveries at night, Sholom saw himself at his post at the gate, hailing a coach pulled by a lively troika of horses.

"Stop!" he cries. The coachman, responding to the boy's call, reins in his spirited steeds. "Hold it!" In the next instant the passengers pour out of the coach, wealthy, bloated, with double chins from eating a lot, with golden chains across their vests. Descending, they wait for their leather suitcases, filled to bursting, each suitcase weighing a ton. In single file they enter the Rabinowitz inn and each asks for a separate room (usually guests at the Rabinowitz inn were poor and slept six in a room). Each requires a samovar for himself. This should give you an inkling of how rich they are! Furthermore, unlike the paupers who usually stop there and never can afford to order anything to eat, each one of *these* passengers requests lunch *and* dinner. Sholom sees his father entering.

"Welcome," Reb Nahum says to each one of the new guests, smiling broadly, pleased. Do they plan to spend the Sabbath?

They will spend several Sabbaths, comes the reply.

Father is very happy. Business has never been so good. The stepmother appears and quickly puts on her silken Sabbath kerchief. She beams on the new guests. She asks who has brought them all, and Sholom, flushed with pride, raises his hand.

What a Sabbath they will have! Not one Sabbath, but several!

The reveries were sweet, the awakening cruel. Entering the house, he saw his father in his shabby robe, bending low over his books. Nearby was the stepmother, working, as usual. "Anyone pass by?" she demanded, cross.

"Yes——"

"Well?"

"As usual they went to Yasnegradski's."

She became enraged. What would now happen to the bread she baked and the fish she cooked? Did Sholom think *he* would eat them? No chance!

Sholom, fearing a storm of abuse, turned on his heel and ran out and resumed his vigil near the gate. There, at least, one found peace. One sat and dreamed of wealthy passengers wrapped in bearskins, of leather bags weighing a ton.

Sitting near the gate, Sholom began to read. The first book he read, one he found by accident, was *Robinson Crusoe*. He liked the book so well that he sat down and wrote a book of his own, calling it *The Jewish Robinson Crusoe*.

One of his father's friends, a man who sold lottery tickets and wore dark glasses and rubbers (he could not afford shoes), and was known in town as The Collector, brought Sholom more books to read. One of them was called *The Love of Zion*. It was a novel in Hebrew by Abraham Mapu, whose works were popular.

Sholom read the book one Saturday afternoon, lying flat on his belly in the attic, underneath the roof. He wept bitterly over the misfortunes of the unhappy Amnon, the book's hero. He muffled his sobs, fearing discovery. And he fell madly in love with the beautiful Tamar, the heroine. He conversed with her in the exalted words of The Song of Songs. He saw her in his dreams. All next day, Sholom was in a daze. He suffered from a violent headache and had no appetite for food.

"What happened to *you?*" his stepmother queried. "I didn't know an appetite like yours could be mislaid."

Sholom ignored her shafts of sarcasm. What could she know about love?

He had to do something! An idea took root in his mind. He would write a book! With the few pennies he'd saved from tips, Sholom bought a ream of paper. He sewed it into a notebook, lining both sides of the paper. He found some pencil stumps, sharpened them and began writing. It was to be a novel, written in the style of Mapu, but the title was to be his own, *The Daughter Of Zion*. The two main characters would be called Solomon and Shulamite; they would be more madly in love than Amnon and Tamar.

Owing to the fact that he spent the first half of

each day in *cheder,* the other half in front of the
gate, Sholom wrote at night. Instead of sleeping, he
wrote. He sat in the attic. Nearby a kerosene lamp
burned dimly. He wrote in a small precise hand. He
was supremely happy until . . . one night his stepmother caught Sholom in the act. She came up
stealthily, walking on tiptoe. Sholom, who was ab-
sorbed by the suffering of his two main characters,
did not hear her.

Her voice burst over Sholom like thunder:
"What's going on here?"

"No-thing——" he stammered, rising.

"This you call nothing?!" She pointed to his writing materials and at the kerosene burning in the
lamp.

"I'm writing a—novel," Sholom confessed.

"A novel!" she screamed. "This—oh—why—
wastrel! Burning precious kerosene—may you burn
at the stake!"

The stepmother's screams awakened the household. There were shouts: "Fire!" "Help!"

She grabbed Sholom's unfinished work. She was
about to tear it up when Reb Nahum, who had come
running, took it from her.

"I'll deal with him," Sholom's father said gravely.

Sholom's heart skipped a beat. He was prepared
for the worst.

What followed was most unexpected. Sholom was
not punished. He was not even reprimanded. Reb
Nahum, instead of destroying the work, showed it to
his friends. One of those consulted was The Collector, who took the manuscript home. On the fol-

lowing day, when The Collector appeared at the inn, his eyes concealed behind the dark glasses, Sholom and his father were waiting impatiently to hear the verdict. The Collector lowered his bulk into a chair, took a deep breath and said to Sholom, "Come here, you rascal."

Sholom obeyed and received a pinch on his cheek. "That's for you," The Collector said with approval. And to Reb Nahum he declared that Sholom was going to grow up to be a *somebody*. And he gave Sholom another approving pinch on the cheek for good measure.

He would be a *somebody!* The notion intoxicated Sholom. A *somebody* meant he would be a writer, like Mapu. The Collector had said so! Sholom and his father put great store by The Collector's words. The man was something of a freethinker, true, but he was a reader of many books. Too bad their friend Arnold did not concur with the others. Arnold, who possessed one of the largest private libraries in Pereyaslav and discoursed on any subject imaginable, came out and said bluntly that he'd read Sholom's *Daughters of Zion* and advised it be thrown in the garbage.

"What do you mean?" Reb Nahum asked with an injured air.

"Such doodling is a waste," Arnold declared. If his friend wanted to make something of the little one, why not send him to the County School?

"County School?" Reb Nahum asked, furrowing his brow. Very few Jewish boys studied at the

County School, as Jewish parents hesitated to send their sons to a Christian institution.

Arnold nodded. In the County School the boy could *learn* something. From there he might go on to a rabbinical school or to a Gymnasium, where he could prepare to be anything, even a doctor.

Sholom was pained by Arnold's words regarding his novel. He respected Arnold, who could speak more eloquently on almost any subject than anyone he knew. Sholom did not like his work consigned to the garbage pile. But the word "Gymnasium" had a warm musical sound. He had heard the word before; in fact, he'd given it some thought. They did not have one such in Pereyaslav. But in the larger cities there were Gymnasia, government high schools whose students wore fine dark uniforms with sparkling brass buttons and caps with visors. Only a very few Jewish boys were admitted to these schools. Jewish parents often spent all they possessed to bribe school officials to admit their sons to the Gymnasia.

Sholom knew of one Jewish boy in Pereyaslav who was fortunate enough to attend a Gymnasium. His name too was Sholom, but everybody called him Solomon. Solomon talked Russian fluently, like a Gentile.

Sholom was eaten up with envy. "Why can't *my* parents afford to send me to a Gymnasium?" Solomon's parents had the means, his father being a doctor. He wasn't really a doctor, only a half-doctor, you might say. There were several doctors in Peryaslav, the Fat Doctor, the Hunchbacked Doctor, the

Black Doctor; they were all Christians. The only one who was Jewish was Yankel, Solomon's father, and he was only a half-doctor. But he behaved as though he were a *full* one. He carried a stethoscope and wrote prescriptions, in Latin, no less. Invariably, he instructed patients to take a tablespoonful of Kali Bromali every two hours. In addition, he suggested a teaspoonful of Natri Bromatri every three hours. By tomorrow morning the patient should feel better. If he did not feel better, he might get worse. In that event, Yankel should be called again.

Everybody in town liked Yankel, including Sholom. When Yankel paid a visit, you could ask him all sorts of questions and he took the trouble to answer. You could ask Yankel why a person suffering from rheumatism of the leg was told to drink fish oil. Yankel replied without hesitation. He possessed a great virtue, he didn't haggle. He took whatever amount you gave him. When you handed Yankel a coin for his visit, he put it in his pocket without examining it. But he had a habit of keeping his hand in the pocket for a while, rubbing the coin with his fingers, trying to determine how much you had given him. If it was less than he thought deserving, Yankel returned it, telling the patient he didn't have to give him anything. But it was plain by his injured air that if the amount were not increased, Yankel would not come back.

Yankel had an additional virtue. He let you talk as much as your heart desired. Nor was he tight-lipped about his own affairs. On the contrary. He talked a blue streak. Best of all, he liked telling about his "wonderful children." His eldest, Sholom—Solomon, that is—attended a Gymnasium. As though you didn't know! "After he completes the Gymnasium," Yankel boasted shamelessly, "he will enter the university. From there he will emerge a doctor, a *real* doctor."

Gymnasia, doctor, uniform, brass buttons! Sholom saw visions of himself transported to another world. In his reveries he changed places with Solomon. In fact, his own name was changed from Sholom to Solomon. Everybody in Pereyaslav was filled with admiration: "That's Reb Nahum Rabinowitz's son, the Gymnasium student, Solomon!" He was the town's sensation, the wonder of wonders.

There was a serious obstacle between himself and the Gymnasia. He was yet to be accepted by the County School.

6 Hope is a soaring bird

Book in hand, Sholom moved about the room, studying Russian. Now that he was a student at the
County School, he was determined to prove to his
father, as well as to Uncle Pinney, who had opposed
Sholom's going there, that he richly deserved the
trust and confidence placed in him. Angry words
had passed between the Rabinowitz brothers about
Sholom's being taken out of *cheder* and sent to a
school filled with Gentiles. Uncle Pinney had raged
and stormed, declaring that Jewish boys who went
to the County School departed so far from the ways
of piety, they even carried handkerchiefs in their
breast pockets on the Sabbath. And instead of con-
versing in the mother tongue, Yiddish, they babbled
in Russian! But Reb Nahum had stood his ground. It
had taken a good deal of soul-searching by this
pious man, reared in the traditional ways of his people, before his mind was made up to send his favorite son to study among Christians.

"Then at least you'll insist that the boy be excused from classes on the Sabbath."

"I will, of course I will."

"And that he not be in the classroom when the priests give them religious instruction."

Reb Baruch had said, "Of course."

Uncle Pinney's misgivings were not fully allayed. He expected nothing but grief to come of Sholom's going to that school. This was unfortunate, as the boy had a good head on his shoulders.

Uncle Pinney never let an opportunity pass to taunt Sholom about the school. "So you're a student at the County School, eh?" he said, his voice heavy with sarcasm. In Reb Student's opinion thunder comes before lightning. But the fact that we see lightning first and thunder comes later, this meant nothing to him! Uncle Pinney sat back and rocked with laughter. Another thing. Sholom claimed the earth was round, like an apple. Could he prove it?

"I will." And he suggested that his uncle get up early in the morning and take a look at the tip of the church steeple as the sun was rising; he would note that the tip lights up before anything else.

"Tip sh-mip!" Uncle Pinney shot back. One would think he had nothing more to do than get up at dawn and stare at the church steeple.

Sholom liked the school. During the first day his Christian classmates seized him in the courtyard and smeared lard on his lips. "Like the taste of pork?" they asked, amused. They roared with laughter each time he opened his mouth to speak Russian. Their laughter embarrassed him. He was not accustomed to the role of a *shlimiel!* In the past, it was he who had laughed at others. He was determined to do something about it.

Now Sholom walked the measure of the room, studying. Nearby, his father, wearing shawl and phylacteries, was praying. The stepmother was busy with her chores. Every now and then she glanced up from her work and sent a verbal thunderbolt at her husband or her stepson. "How come," she addressed Reb Nahum, "you told me you had six children instead of twelve?"

Reb Nahum ignored the query. He stood facing the wall, muttering his prayers.

She made one more attempt to rouse him, gave up and turned to Sholom, demanding his help.

Sholom, intimidated, put down the book and asked what she wanted him to do?

"Take the samovar."

Suddenly Reb Nahum spun on his heel. "Leave him alone!" he shouted, livid with rage. His eyes, fastened on the stepmother, were like hot black coals. His lower lip trembled. The angry words were spoken in Hebrew, as he was in the midst of prayer. She was to leave him alone. . . . He didn't care if she ordered his other children to do chores. But not Sholom! He was to study!

"Yes, Nahum." She retreated, stunned. She had never heard his voice so filled with anger, so menacing.

On the following morning, her voice and manner seemed to Sholom strangely different, almost unrecognizable. She greeted him warmly and did not ask him to do any chores. From that time on, she would only nag him on occasion and accuse him of wasting a pound of paper and three bottles of ink every week—but she ceased giving him chores.

At school, too, fortune briefly turned her smiling countenance upon him. One morning the director of the school sent for Sholom's father.

Reb Nahum dressed quickly. He put on his Sabbath mantle, tucked the sidecurls behind his ears and ran to school. Why were they summoning him? Was Sholom behind in his work? Were they going to expel Sholom?

When he arrived, Reb Nahum was informed that his son had won a prize of 120 rubles for being an outstanding student. Reb Nahum wept with joy.

In Pereyaslav Sholom's achievement created a sensation. The first Jewish boy to win such a prize, his name was on everybody's lips. People came to the inn in large numbers to congratulate Reb Nahum and gaze at the winner. Strangers as well as acquaintances stroked his hair. The Collector stared at Sholom through his dark glasses, pinched his cheek and called him "rascal." Then he repeated his earlier prophecy that some day Sholom would be a *somebody*.

At home there was a party. Uncle Pinney came with his sons and Aunt Hannah with her daughters. What was he going to do with all that money? they asked.

Sholom knew exactly what he would do with it. He would give the 120 rubles to his father. Recently

his father had started making wines to supplement
their meager income from the inn. He made the wines
himself, in their cellar, from raisins and a syrup he
concocted in secret. And he gave them names:
"Madeira," "Sherry," "Kosher for Passover," and
so on. Over the door of his modest establishment he
hung a sign: WINES FROM SOUTHERN SHORES. With
Sholom's 120 rubles the business could be expanded.

Everybody at the party sang Sholom's praises. He
was supremely happy. It appeared as though his
rich dreams were becoming reality. He was on his
way now—to becoming a *somebody*. The path leading to glory was broad and clear. He glanced at his
father, who was transformed, by some stroke of
magic, into a young man. His back seemed straight
and the wrinkles were gone from his forehead. He
did not sigh once all evening. It was a joy to behold
him.

For Sholom the County School opened many
doors to strange and fascinating worlds. He plunged
eagerly into the study of geography and mathe-
matics. There too he experienced the happiness of
one of his most deeply felt friendships.

Ali was a classmate. The first words spoken between them were in the street one evening as both of
them were chasing after volunteer fire-fighters.

"Here they come!" one said to the other with the
informality prevailing in a crowded street.

"Let's run after them and see what happens."

Afterward, they became inseparable. They sat
near each other in the classroom, did their home-

work together, played during leisure time. On their days off, they spent many hours floating in a rowboat on the mirrorlike surface of the river. They rested in the tall green grass, read books, sang songs, dreamed of a rich, meaningful future. Where would they go after graduating? There wasn't any doubt in their minds about graduating, as they were the brightest students in the school (as well as the biggest mischief-makers). What subjects would they study? What careers would they pursue? It occurred to neither, at the time, that their plans might miscarry.

One term flowed into the next. Graduation was almost at hand. Sholom looked forward to the end. He was eager for new challenges. Every now and then he gave some thought to the career he would choose. To be a writer appealed to him immensely. But he would not become a writer unless Ali too chose to be one. And Ali did not seem eager. Sholom could not conceive of a future without Ali. In his opinion, nobody was so good as his friend, so bright and talented. Take such a thing as making people laugh. Ali was a comic the likes of which Sholom had not seen before. Moreover, he was an actor, a mimic who imitated all their teachers. Sholom couldn't stop laughing at Ali's antics. A mimic himself, he conceded first place to his friend. But they had their serious moments.

After they finished the County School, Sholom suggested, they could both go to a Gymnasium. They could go on to a university to study medicine or law or engineering; *anything,* as long as they remained together.

At the inn, where Reb Nahum drank tea with his friends and played an occasional game of chess, the only topic of discussion was: Where would Sholom go to continue his studies? They talked of nothing else. Reb Nahum's mind was scarcely on his business. "What's to be done?" he said over and over again.

"We'll send him to the Teachers' Institute at Zhitomir," The Collector said with his usual air of confidence.

The idea appealed to Reb Nahum. The Collector suggested that he sit down right now and write them a letter, a nice long letter, in Hebrew. And tell them in Zhitomir about this rascal of theirs. They'll grab him in no time at all.

Reb Nahum brought pen and ink and sat down to write the letter. He worked slowly, perspiring as he wrote. This letter *had* to be good! His favorite son's future was at stake.

The Collector stood in back of the letter writer, peering at the paper through his dark glasses. He read the Hebrew words as Reb Nahum committed them to paper. "Good!" he said. When Reb Nahum was finally done, The Collector exclaimed: "An excellent letter, my friend! That should do it!" He sank into a chair, took off his glasses and wiped them. Now the rascal was all set! Whether he was going to be a teacher or a rabbi, one thing was certain, he was going to be a somebody! His nearsighted eyes fastened on Reb Nahum's forehead, which was a maze of wrinkles. "What is the matter?" he asked.

"The draft," Reb Nahum said with concern. "I can't get it out of my mind. The army is likely to take him."

"Not a chance!" the Collector said emphatically. Government *rabbiners* and those who taught in government schools were exempt from the draft.

"I hope what you say is right."

"I know it's right," The Collector said. Now, all that remained to be done was to find Sholom a pretty bride with a decent dowry. And he'd be set for life. The Collector laughed and clapped his hands. "What do you say to a glass of your excellent Madeira wine, Reb Nahum?"

The two friends drank a toast to Sholom's bright future.

Several days later the crushing blow fell. A letter arrived from Zhitomir. They opened and read it, all of them anticipating a favorable reply. Instead, it was a rejection, the letter-writer stating that whereas the Institute course was of four years' duration, and whereas the applicant's papers stated he was born February 18, 1859, making him subject to the draft in October, 1880, three years from now, thus preventing him from completing his studies, therefore the Institute reluctantly rejected his application for admission.

"On account of a few months," Reb Nahum cried, "they are ruining him."

Sholom lived as though in a nightmare. He sensed that an epoch was ending. Ali, several months younger than himself, had been accepted by the Institute. Ali was leaving. Their paths might never again flow together. Never. Gone was the dream of sharing a room in the strange city of Zhitomir, of reading Byron and Lermontov together, of marching, hands clasped, toward a bright future. It had all been a dream, a false dream. . . .

7 The cantor's daughter

He was still at the County School when it happened.
He met her on one of his frequent walks with his
friend Ali. It occurred on the Sabbath, after prayers,
when many Jewish boys and girls were drawn to the
river and dallied on the bridge. The boys and the
girls started toward the river in separate groups.
When they reached their destination and were now
far enough from the prying eyes of their parents,
they stopped to talk.

She smiled at him one Sabbath afternoon and he
smiled back. When they next met, he boldly said
hello. She nodded in response and walked on with
her girl friend. He waited a full week before seeing
her again. This time he took his life in his hands and
inquired after her health.

She replied, "I'm fine," and blushed.

Now they were acquainted. And now when they
met on the bridge, they stopped for a minute or two
to talk. When they were about to part, Sholom flung

caution to the winds and said, ''I hope to see you again.''

She asked whether he had next Sabbath in mind.

He replied: When else?

She asked whether they would meet again on the bridge.

He answered: Where else?

She had a special place in mind, she said. The Cold Synagogue, where her father was the cantor.

He promised to meet her at the Cold Synagogue on Simchas Torah.

He went home to count the passing days, hours and minutes. Finally Simchas Torah burst upon them in all its glory. Sholom prepared early for the synagogue. Instead of accompanying his father to the Big Synagogue, he escaped without a word.

The Cold Synagogue was a large, lofty place, without a ceiling, but with a roof (which was the reason it was known as the Cold Synagogue). The inside of the roof was painted to look like a sky, a blue sky. This particular sky was a little too blue, almost green. The artist, it was obvious, had over-played his hand. Moreover, the shining stars in this sky were a bit oversize. Each star looked as large as a potato, gilded at the edges. The potatoes—that is, the stars—instead of being flung across the heavens, were arranged in neat rows.

The place was packed with men and women and children, all shouting, talking and laughing at the same time. But where was she?

Sholom felt uneasy. Why wasn't she there? Why wasn't her friend and constant companion there?

Was it possible she was deceiving him? Perhaps some dreadful accident had happened to her on the way. . . . Perhaps her father, Tzali the Cantor, had prevented her from coming. Morbid thoughts raced through Sholom's mind.

Suddenly she appeared out of the dense crowd. He was holding the Torah scroll, a signal honor for a boy his age, when she appeared. She bent down and kissed his hand. It was a quick touch of the lips but he felt as though he had been touched by fire. Was it an accident? Had she really meant to kiss his hand and not the scroll? No, it was not an accident! He could tell by her smiling eyes. He returned her smile. He was borne on wings. Angels soared with him toward the "sky" and past it. Suddenly she vanished in the crowd.

Sholom went home in a daze. He must see her again! But how? Wait until next Saturday and hope to meet on the bridge? An eternity lay between now and then.

He decided to write her a letter. He spent a whole day and most of the night composing the note. After he had finished, his heart was revealed on the pages. Now the question arose: how to get the letter to her? Ask her friend to give it to her? If he asked the friend, she would learn their secret. Could he rely on the friend to transmit the letter to the cantor's daughter without reading it? But even if he wished to use her as a messenger, Sholom would first have to find out how to get in touch with her. Fortunately she knew a boy who worked in a hardware store. Thus, a fourth person would become involved. But

Sholom had no alternative. He put the letter in his pocket and went to the hardware store. The boy was husky, with huge hands, and not particularly friendly. He asked Sholom who sent him.

"Your girl," Sholom replied.

"How do you know I have a girl?"

Sholom informed the clerk he was acquainted with her friend, the cantor's daughter.

"That one is a real whizzer!" the clerk said.

Sholom inquired what he meant by the remark but the clerk smiled, turning his question aside. Instead, he wanted to know what brought Sholom to the store.

Sholom fumbled in his pocket, took out the sealed envelope, gave it to the clerk with trembling hand and begged him to tell the recipient of the letter that a reply was requested.

The clerk took the letter, folded it roughly, shoved it in his pocket and, brusquely dismissing Sholom, asked him to come back tomorrow.

On the following day Sholom appeared early at the store, but there was no reply. He came the next day. Again, no reply.

Several days passed without a reply. Sholom lived as though suspended in mid-air. He did not eat or sleep.

Toward the end of the week the clerk handed him a sealed envelope. "From her," he said with a smirk.

Sholom seized the letter and ran out of the store. Outside, alone, his heart racing wildly, he opened the letter and read: "Tears were in my eyes," the

cantor's daughter wrote, "each time I read your letter." If she had wings, she would fly to be with him.
If she could swim, she would swim to him. She
warned him not to write to her again; eyes for which
his letter was not meant had read it.

Then it happened! The disaster struck Sholom
without warning. Several days after Simchas Torah
and the love letter, the cantor's daughter ran away
from home. This blow Sholom might have endured.
But the cantor's daughter did not leave home alone.
She ran off with a Gentile!

The tragic news spread like a fire through Pereyaslav. THE CANTOR'S DAUGHTER . . . WITH A GENTILE!
She's going to marry him——She's entered a nun-
nery for the purpose of being baptized, so she can
marry him. There's nothing left to do but to excom-
municate her. Poor Tzali the Cantor!

At first Sholom refused to believe it. It could not
be! But when he saw Tzali, grief-stricken, his face a
mask of despair, Sholom knew the truth. He ran
home, his heart filled with bitterness and hate. He
hated the cantor's daughter for betraying him. He
hated the whole wicked world. . . .

He was feverish. A glassy stare was in his eyes.
The world spun around and made him dizzy. He
refused food. He collapsed and was put to bed. He
heard disembodied words floating about his bed: doctor, stomach, apothecary. And his head spun and
spun around. Nightmare mingled with reality and he
did not know which was which. Before him stood his

friends Shmulik, Ali and the others. And there was the cantor's daughter, the apostate. . . .

His lips were dry and cracked and he talked in his fever. When finally he rose from the sickbed, Sholom's cheeks were gaunt. His curly blond hair had been shorn and his skull appeared naked. He gazed at himself in the mirror and saw a stranger. Inside too, there had been a transformation. He was no longer a boy. He was now a young man.

8 The tutor

He was almost seventeen. Soft hair was beginning to sprout on his upper lip. His head was crammed full of knowledge. How was he to make use of the storehouse of information?

"Why don't you become a tutor?" one of his father's friends suggested.

"A tutor?" It had not occurred to him. Who would want him?

"With *your* knowledge of Russian and grammar!"

"You really think so?"

He was surprised how many people sought him to tutor their children. He began coaching children as well as grownups; "giving hours" it was called. He was very busy. It seemed as though everybody in Pereyaslav, young as well as old, was preparing for some kind of an exam. Learning among the Jews was the rage; it assumed the proportions of an epidemic. Jewish parents who could afford it, and many who could not, hired tutors to coach their sons, as well as daughters, to prepare them for the higher institutions of learning; this was in the face of a rigid quota system maintained by the Gymnasia, accepting one Jewish student to a ratio of ten Christians. The Latin name for this brutal exclusion was *numerus clausus*.

In all of Pereyaslav there were only two tutors. Old Monisoff, who had no teeth in his mouth and spat instead of talking and was stone deaf, was one of them. The other was Boosel, a young man who gave French lessons and charged exorbitant fees. There were also the two brothers, Yitzi the Writer and Abraham the Writer, who taught for a pittance. Unfortunately they were weak in grammar. And as grammar was considered as important as breathing itself, the brothers had very few students. Even Sholom's Uncle Pinney, the pious one, conceded that grammar was "a good thing." "But what I fail to understand," Uncle Pinney argued, "is why you grammarians insist on walking around without a cap to cover your heads, why you sit down to eat without washing your hands, why you write on the Sabbath!"

Sholom's reputation as a tutor grew. Parents besieged his father to prevail upon him to spare an hour, a half-hour for their sons. It was known in all of Pereyaslav that Sholom had a way with grammar and prepared you for examinations better than anyone.

Sholom ranged all over town tutoring. There were coins in his pockets now—not many, but enough to make him feel grown-up. He bought books and carried a cane. At night he sat in the room he shared with some of his brothers and read.

The stepmother complained that he would ruin them by burning so much kerosene at night.

He was no longer intimidated by her. He did not fight back, nor did he judge her harshly. She was overworked, caring for her large brood of children as well as the inn. Eager to strike out on his own and not feel indebted to anyone, Sholom counted the coins in his pocket and went out to find a room. To have a room all to himself made him feel the master of his own destiny. The one he found was adequate, the kerosene supply unlimited. He could stay up all night reading. In return, he taught several of his landlord's children.

The worst part of leaving home was parting with his father. Reb Nahum was saddened over his son's moving out. But he acquiesced when Sholom promised to come every Sabbath.

"Every Sabbath," Reb Nahum repeated.

Many years later, long after he'd left Pereyaslav, Sholom Aleichem recalled the joyous occasions, the Sabbath afternoons he spent with his father and others, sitting at the dinner table, talking about books, philosophy, religion, reading poetry aloud. His father, although he could hardly afford it, usually had two guests, in addition to Sholom, at the Sabbath table. One of the guests was The Collector. Bniminsohn, known as The Poet, was the final member of the quartet. He was a spare man with a long neck which reminded Sholom of a goose each time he swallowed a morsel of food. The Poet, who wrote in Hebrew, slept in the corridor of the Rabinowitz inn. He could not afford to spend more than a penny each day for a herring, which he liked to toast on the coals in the oven. "Let's get rid of him," the step-mother urged more than once, offended by the acrid smell of The Poet's herrings.

But Reb Nahum, a man of deep compassion, put her off. "Where will the poor man go?" he asked.

Only once a week did The Poet eat a full meal, on the Sabbath, at Reb Nahum's table. He ate and re-cited his poetry.

Sholom looked forward eagerly to these gather-ings. Treated as a grownup, no longer called a rascal by The Collector, he sat with the others, an equal among them. There was little in common between a man like Nahum Rabinowitz, a half-Chasid and half-Maskil [follower of the Enlightenment], and such a person as The Collector, a Litvak, a *mith-nagid* [one who opposed the Chasidim as being too emotional in worshipping God]. Nor did there seem any common ground between those two and the starved poet, Bniminsohn. And how did Sholom fit in, he who was so much younger than the others? And yet, there they were, the four of them, bound by a firm friendship, each one of them looking for-ward to the Sabbath, and the intimacy that bound them. When something out of the ordinary hap-pened to one of them, he would guard it like a price-less jewel until the Sabbath, to share it with the others. Sholom hoped these meetings would be part of his life forever. But they ended abruptly, in the most unforseen fashion.

One day The Collector died. Sholom and his fa-ther had not even known that he was ill. He was in the habit of absenting himself from the inn for days

on end, eventually to reappear. This time he failed
to come to a Sabbath dinner. His friends became
suspicious. They inquired about him and found out
he was dead. Sholom felt bereaved. This was a man
of whom Sholom knew little, yet he had been like a
second father to him, a patron who by word and
deed made the boy feel he would become a "somebody." Accompanied by his father, Sholom went
down to the cellar where The Collector had made his
home for many years. They held on to a damp wall,
going down. They opened the door to his room and
saw on a bare floor, lying in a heap, an object covered by a sheet. At the head, two candles burned fit-
fully in two bottles of different sizes and colors.
Nearby, sitting in an old rickety chair, was an old
Jew with an unkempt beard and torn frock, praying. Near the wall, Sholom caught sight of the old
torn rubbers and on the sill of the only window were
The Collector's large black glasses. These were his
earthly possessions. To those who did not know him,
and this included most of Pereyaslav, it appeared
that this was all he had left behind. But Sholom and
his father, who loved the man, knew in their hearts
that he had left behind a great deal more.

The funeral was held the same day. It appeared as
though nobody would come. There was no reason to
hope that anyone would come. The deceased had
not been wealthy; on the contrary, he had been so
poor that he could not afford to buy a pair of shoes.
He had not been pious. Far from it. In fact, he had
the reputation of being something of a freethinker.
Moreover, he was a stranger, all the way from

Lithuania. Sholom and his father expected nobody to come. But they were determined that he should have a proper funeral. They ran around town, imploring people to attend the funeral. As they both had many friends among the intelligentsia, the funeral procession soon turned into a who-is-who of Pereyaslav. Some of the town's foremost citizens came. The curious began to gather. Beggars, cripples assembled, seeking alms. They carried on noisily, demanding explanations as to why nobody gave them money. It was hard to convince them that the deceased had been as much a pauper as they.

The courtyard of the synagogue filled up with people. The streets were jammed. People asked one another, "Were you notified of this?"

There weren't any tears. Nobody was seen to rend his garments, nobody heard reciting *Kaddish*.

It was a silent, proper funeral. Sholom was pleased, he was grateful to God that people were repaying in kind, if not during one's lifetime, then after death. What was being done for The Collector, the honor bestowed, was little enough. It made Sholom wish The Collector could rise for an instant from his eternal sleep, put on his dark glasses and gaze at the throng paying homage to him. . . .

It was one of the most imposing funerals witnessed by the people of Pereyaslav.

Soon after the funeral, The Poet too left. He disappeared without telling them where he was going.

Sholom felt keenly the loss of these two. With his friend Ali gone to Zhitomir, he felt alone. For him Pereyaslav became a desert.

9 Away from home

An out-of-town guest said to Reb Nahum, "I wish you would convince your son to come to our town and teach my children. Believe me, I'll treat him as though he were my own. I'll treat him like a king. He'll be able to name his own price."

"I'll go," Sholom said without any hesitation. He was eager to get away from Pereyaslav. A change of scenery might do him good.

Reb Nahum decided to accompany his son all the way. They sailed on a small steamer. When they arrived they were received like royalty. Their host, a dealer in animal skins, and his wife, who was an excellent cook, fed father and son magnificently, stuffing them full of fish, meat, fowl and desserts. Sholom had not eaten so well since Voronko, during their days of affluence. At night, their beds were made on soft couches covered with silk.

On the following day, Sholom's father made ready to go back to Pereyaslav. "This appears to be a good position," he said to his son before leaving.

Sholom escorted his father to the pier and returned to the house alone.

He was surprised to find the meal simple, almost frugal, as compared with those served when his father was there. Instead of putting him to sleep on the soft couch, as on the previous night, Sholom's bed was made on top of an iron box. In the morning he got up stiff-necked, his bones aching.

Sholom was disappointed at the sudden turn of events, but he said nothing. For breakfast he was given hardly anything to eat; for the midday meal he was shocked to find a solitary potato, nothing more; in the evening he had only bread and tea. That night he was put to bed on the floor, on some pelts. The ill-smelling skins nauseated him. A colicky infant in a cradle nearby began to scream. Unable to sleep, Sholom spent the long hours of the night trying to pacify the baby.

Reduced to performing menial tasks, Sholom rebelled. "I came here to teach, not to——"

"Of course, of course," his employer tried to mollify him.

"I was up all last night with the poor baby," Sholom complained.

"I'm sorry. It won't happen again," the man assured him.

When Sholom was getting ready for sleep that night, he found himself again in the same room with the screaming baby. In the morning he reeled from fatigue. I'm leaving, he decided.

He left the pelt dealer's employment and took a

position in another household. He found it no better
than the first. His new employers insisted that he
perform menial tasks in addition to tutoring their
children. He quit and went elsewhere. Everywhere
he was treated like a servant. He was insulted,
abused and reviled. Town gossips invented cruel
stories about him. The ordeal of staying there was
more than he could bear. But he put off going back
until the end of the term.

Coming home was in the nature of a defeat.
Pereyaslav was not the same. His friends had all
gone away. Those who had not left home appeared a
little older. He felt older too. He dressed according
to the latest style, in a soft gray hat, short coat and
long, wide trousers. His shoes had elevated heels. He
wore his blond hair long, combed back straight, like
a poet. He gave the outward appearance of being
pleased with himself. In reality, Sholom was very
unhappy. For one who had savored being on his
own, even if only briefly, it was difficult to reconcile
himself to being supported by his father.

"This is your home," Reb Nahum assured him. He
took pride in a son who read Darwin and discoursed
eloquently on evolution, literature and anything else
you cared to mention. The stepmother, on the other
hand, made no secret of the fact that Sholom was an
idler, more concerned with books than earning his
keep.

Sholom walked the streets of Pereyaslav, despair
his companion. There was an emptiness in his heart.
He felt drained of all energy. Living became tire-
some. All his dreams were ashes.

When an offer finally came of a position in a distant town, Sholom said he would take it. It was not even an offer, but more in the nature of a rumor. One of Reb Nahum's friends declared one day that he knew of a fabulously rich man who lived near the town of K. and was looking for a tutor in the worst way. He wanted a teacher who knew Russian as well as Yiddish.

The conversation established one fact: Reb Nahum was acquainted with the fabulously rich man. When Sholom's father knew him, he was a little nobody.

"He has coffers of gold now," the friend assured Sholom's father. "And he's tearing his hair out trying to find the proper teacher for his children. Don't you think you had better do something about it?"

Reb Nahum sat down without delay and wrote to his old acquaintance, the fabulously rich man. Written in Hebrew, the letter was a model of eloquence and penmanship. It was a document that could move a stone, Sholom thought. If the fabulously rich man had only a few of the virtues attributed to him in the letter, he would be a rare person indeed.

Sholom pocketed the letter and boarded a train. He had only a very little money in his wallet. Whatever he had earned tutoring, he had spent long ago, most of it on his stylish clothes. But he was not inclined to worry. Wasn't the job a sure thing? Armed with his father's priceless letter, he was certain to achieve his mission.

He arrived at his destination toward evening. When he got off the train, Sholom was mildly disappointed to find that his prospective employer lived a long distance from town. Having no money, he began walking. He was keenly aware of the scented country air and filled his lungs with it. He felt free, purposeful again, bent on conquest. He would begin earning money again, no later than tomorrow.

A tall forbidding fence loomed up before him. He spied a gate nearby. A guard with a large peasant face stood in front of the gate. A dog with fangs bared sprang up at Sholom's approach, straining at its leash.

"I have a letter to the master," Sholom began, keeping a respectful distance from the dog. (On his body there was still a mark where a dog belonging to a Christian had once bit him; his first contact with anti-Semitism, he called it.)

The guard, who had vacant eyes and an unpleasant smile, came forward and took the letter from Sholom. He rang a bell and a servant came out of the large house. The servant took the letter, gazed at the envelope, then at the young stranger and said, "How about me?"

"But I have no money," Sholom pleaded.

"Then the letter will not be delivered."

"But it's very important! Your master is expecting this letter." Frantically he searched in his pockets. He took out his empty wallet. "Here."

The servant was about to refuse but changed his mind. "Wait here," he said, taking Sholom's wallet and pocketing it.

"Can't I wait inside?"

"Outside," the guard said.

Sholom took up a position just beyond the reach of the dog. The road to paradise, he reflected, often was a rocky one. His heart beat wildly as he saw the servant emerging from the house.

"Did you deliver the letter?"

"Yes."

"And?"

"And what?"

"Where's the reply?"

"No reply," the servant said. "First my master has to read the letter," he explained, "and when that will be I don't know. My master is a busy man." He might have added that even if his master were not busy, he would not read the letter, as he did not know Hebrew.

Sholom retreated, disappointed. Not today, he thought, he'll read it tomorrow. After all, he a fabulously wealthy man and must be very busy.

He started toward town. Where would he spend the night? He could not sleep in the open. He inquired at several inns, but their keepers refused to give him lodging unless he paid in advance. Sholom was about to give up when he found a man who offered to put him up. His name was Red Berl and he was the town's outstanding busybody.

"What are you doing in town?" Red Berl probed.

"Visiting."

"For what purpose?"

"No purpose."

Berl touched his red beard reflectively. "You

aren't here to see the fabulously rich man, are you?''

''Why should I want to see him?'' Sholom parried,
resenting Berl's probing.

''Many people come here to see him,'' Berl replied
calmly, ''especially lately. Young tutors and old
tutors, from nearby towns and faraway towns. It's
been rumored that he's looking for a teacher. So
there's been a rush. Poor, hungry devils. What a
pity.'' He looked searchingly at Sholom. ''You don't
happen to be one of them, do you?''

Sholom did not reply. The words ''poor, hungry''
struck him with especial force. There was no question about it, he was hungry, having gone without
food since noon. Pride prevented him from admitting it.

''We're getting ready to sit down for a bite,'' Red
Berl said. ''Come, join us.''

''No, thank you, I'm not hungry,'' Sholom lied. He
went to the tiny room where he would spend the
night and lay down. He was too hungry to fall
asleep. The strong sweet odors of food reached him
all the way from the dining room. The odors pursued and teased him. He clamped two fingers on his
nostrils.

He slept. He had a dream and in it appeared the
fabulously rich man. In Sholom's dream, the letter had been delivered and read. And the rich one
was so impressed he hired Sholom not as a tutor but
as his manager to oversee the vast estate. And
Sholom wrote a note to his father, in Hebrew, of
course, for that was the language of the enlightened,
and in the envelope he inserted several crackling

one-hundred ruble notes—a little gift for the holidays. . . . Let his father know he was making head-
way in the world. . . . In the letter, he did not fail to
mention that three spirited horses had been put at
his disposal by the employer. When the townspeople
saw him driving by, they inquired, "Who was that
who just streaked by?"

And upon being told, they would reply that he
was such a young fellow and already so important!

Light peered through the smudged window.
Sholom sat up in bed. He started getting dressed but
a weakness in his limbs overwhelmed him. Hunger
took hold of him and held him in its grip. He went
downstairs, holding on to the rail.

"Would you like tea and a roll?" Red Berl inquired.

"I'm not hungry." In the next instant he was outside, walking unsteadily toward the estate with the
high fence.

"He hasn't read it yet," Sholom was told. He retraced his steps and came back in the early afternoon.

"He hasn't read it."

Despondent, Sholom went back to town. His mind
refused to dwell on the consequences of his failure
to see the fabulously rich man. He was too hungry
to care about anything but food. The question was
how to get hold of food. Frantically he began
searching his pockets for some object he might sell
or exchange for a morsel of food. His mind traced a
course to the watch in his pocket. He would pawn

the watch, dear though it was to him. He had bought it during the period when he had many students in Pereyaslav. He'd paid the staggering sum of twenty-five rubles for it. Now he would pawn it. But where? Suddenly he recalled passing a watch repair shop earlier in the day. He would try the place. He did not expect to receive nearly so much as he had paid for it. He was prepared to take what was offered, being in no position to bargain.

He found the shop, went in and asked the old proprietor behind the counter whether he had any good watches.

The watchmaker, slightly deaf, cocked his good ear at the young stranger and asked how many watches the young man needed.

Sholom said he needed one watch.

"That we have," the old man said, nodding. Did the young man want a gold or a silver watch?

Right now a silver one would do, so long as it was in good order, came the reply.

The watchmaker placed a half dozen sparkling new watches on the counter before his youthful visitor.

Sholom looked at the timepieces critically, chose one and said, "This one will do. Tell you what! I'll give you my watch in exchange for this one if you throw in a couple of rubles in the bargain."

The old man shook his head solemnly. He removed a wad of cotton from one ear and transferred it to the other and said, "As you want two rubles for your watch and I want nine for mine, you give me seven rubles and the deal is made."

Sholom conceded it was a fair offer, to which he would now make a counteroffer. "I'll take two rubles for my watch now and in a day or two I'll come in and give you seven for yours. How's that?"

"No good."

"Why not?" Sholom asked, dismayed.

"Because I'm not a buyer of watches. I sell them."

"Well, suppose we do it this way," Sholom suggested. "I'll *give* you my watch for one ruble, give it to you, that's all."

"Give it to me, why?" the old man wanted to know, suspicion lurking in his eyes.

"Not for money or anything like that," Sholom explained, "a ruble, after all, is not money. I'm giving it to you because I'm disgusted with that watch. I can't bear to look at it."

"In that case, why don't you throw it in the gutter?"

Sholom left the store feeling faint. He doubted having the strength to reach his room at Red Berl's. His knees buckled and his brain was in a whirl. He hoped Berl would not notice him. Berl was the only person in town who knew of his great hunger. If he had money, he would buy a roll or a stale piece of bread and if there were any left over, he would buy a railroad ticket home. But he had no money, not even a penny. He doubted that he would survive the day. Red Berl was willing to feed him, but he wanted no charity.

Sholom started toward the inn. He walked rapidly, with all his remaining strength. He was suddenly in a hurry. He went in stealthily, crept to his room, opened a drawer and took out his prayer shawl and phylacteries. A strong desire surged in him to pray. Tears were in his eyes.

A small synagogue, the town's only prayer-house, was not far away. Did he have the strength to get there? It was important that he get to the synagogue!

His knees wobbled. His head spun. He went into the synagogue. It was empty, except for the beadle who sat in a dark corner repairing shoes, an occupation he pursued when not busy with the affairs of the synagogue. He regarded the unexpected young visitor with curiosity, noting the drawn face and bloodshot eyes. "Do you have *yarzeit?* [Do you wish to say the yearly prayer for the dead?]" the man inquired. "If you do, I'll run and find a *minyan* [ten Jews]."

The young visitor shook his head. He just wanted to pray.

"Help yourself," the beadle said, handing Sholom a prayer book.

Sholom put on his phylacteries, draped the prayer shawl over his shoulders and began to pray. The words spilled from him in a torrent. He could not recall ever praying with such passion and abandon, shedding so many tears. Why the tears? He had no rational way of explaining it. But it felt good to cry. An unbearable weight was off his shoulders. It struck him that he felt less hungry.

Finishing his prayer, Sholom dried his eyes, sighed deeply, put away his phylacteries and folded his shawl. His mind was made up. He was done with

this wilderness of a town. "I'm going home," he said
to himself, "even if I have to walk." He realized he
was returning to Pereyaslav empty-handed and de-
feated. But there wasn't a thing he could do about it.
He would not spend another minute in this town.

Sholom thanked the beadle and started toward
the exit. Outside, he turned his face toward the road.

"Wait a minute."

Startled by the voice, Sholom turned.

Red Berl stood before him.

"I'll send you the money I owe for the room,"
Sholom said quickly. "You don't have to worry
about——"

"I didn't come here to demand what you owe me,"
Berl replied.

"Then what do you want?"

"I have news that should interest you."

"I . . . I don't believe it. I——"

"A distant relative of yours just arrived in town,
and——"

A relative of his? Sholom doubted Berl's words.
"I have no relatives in this town."

"This one doesn't live here," Berl explained,
"he's passing through. I advise you to see him."

"I don't want to see him," Sholom declared, "him
or anyone else. I want only to get out of here." He
started walking.

"Wait a minute."

"Please leave me alone."

"You come with me," Red Berl insisted. He had
hold of Sholom's arm. He was leading him toward
the inn.

Sholom resisted, then gave up. He let Red Berl lead him as though he were a sheep being taken to the slaughterhouse.

They went into the inn. "Go in the next room, the big one," Berl commanded, shoving the unsteady young tutor past a door.

Entering, Sholom saw a stranger two or three years his senior. The young man sat comfortably at a large table, drinking tea from a glass. He was immaculately dressed in expensive clothes. His small round beard was neatly combed. Sholom's eyes wandered from the wealthy stranger to the cakes and pastries on the table.

"My name is Joshua Loyeff," the man said, rising and extending his hand. If Sholom was Reb Nahum's son, from Pereyaslav, Loyeff said, then they were relatives—distant, but relatives.

Sholom nodded, his eyes riveted on the food. He heard Loyeff say something about a cousin or an aunt who was in some way related to his father. He was dimly aware that Red Berl appeared in the room, went out and came back with a glass and a saucer, that Red Berl forcibly lowered him into a chair opposite Loyeff, that tea had been poured for him, that more cakes had been brought and that he was devouring them, several at a time.

Loyeff waited patiently as Sholom sated his voracious appetite, then asked him what he was doing in town.

"I came here to take a position," Sholom replied, ashamed of his gluttony, "as a tutor to a very wealthy man's children."

Joshua Loyeff nodded. "Talking about a tutor, my father is looking for one, to coach my sister. Would you be interested?"

Sholom asked the man to repeat his words. It seemed to him that the stranger was offering him a position, but he was not certain. Was he awake or dreaming?

Loyeff repeated the words. Now Sholom knew beyond any doubt that he was being offered a job. His heart beat wildly. He wanted to shout and to weep. Then he heard himself saying, "Your offer has merit, but on the other hand——"

"I assure you my father is in a position to pay you as much as the man here," Loyeff interrupted.

"I'll have to think about it," Sholom declared, determined not to show his eagerness.

"Think about it?" Red Berl cried, annoyed. "What's there to think about?" Turning to Loyeff, he stated: "He accepts your offer! He gladly accepts it!"

An hour after the chance meeting, Sholom was seated in a comfortable coach, going with his new friend on a journey that altered the course of his life.

10 One foot in paradise

They arrived at their destination in the evening. "You'll meet my father," Joshua Loyeff said as both of them went into a well-appointed inn.

The impression old Loyeff made on Sholom was extraordinary. It never occurred to him that a Jew could look like this man. He had the appearance of a general, better still—a field marshal. His voice was that of a lion.

In a few words, Joshua told his father about Sholom. The old man placed a pair of silver-rimmed glasses on his nose and regarded Sholom with lively curiosity, as though he were inspecting a fish just brought home from the market place. Suddenly thrusting out a huge paw, he inquired: "To what name do you answer?"

"Sholom——"

Nodding with approval, he called the young tutor Sholom-heart, and told him to go into the next room and wash; he had some business to attend to, and when he was done they would have a talk. "Agreed?"

Sholom nodded. How could one disagree with a field marshal? He went into the next room and sat down. Too nervous to sit still, he got up and began pacing the room. He wondered what the old man would ask him. Would he give a good accounting of himself? He heard the door and started. Old Loyeff's gigantic figure was in the doorway.

"Sit down."

Sholom obeyed.

According to his son, old Loyeff said in his booming voice, Sholom was as well versed in Russian as he was in the Bible. Was that true?

Sholom nodded, adding, "True."

That being the case, Loyeff said, he wanted to ask Sholom something out of Rashi's commentaries.

"Please go ahead."

The old man stated his question. Sholom flung back a reply.

"Now let's see about the Gemmorah," Loyeff said, pleased.

There, too, Sholom acquitted himself splendidly.

"Good, good," Reb Elimelech said with approval, maintaining a stern air. "There's one thing that bothers me."

"What's that?" Sholom asked, concerned.

A man could be versed in the Bible and in Hebrew, Reb Elimelech complained, but when it came to writing a decent letter in Russian, he didn't know how. He regarded the young man slyly. "Can you write Russian?"

"What do you want me to write?"

Old Loyeff handed Sholom pen and paper, pointed to a writing desk and instructed Sholom to write a letter to an imaginary sugar factory and tell the manager he would not receive any beets until he remitted such and such amount of money due.

Sholom nodded and began writing. Old Loyeff paced the room until Sholom had finished. He took the letter, read it and boomed: "Good! Now——"

The note, written in impeccable Russian, did not bring the examination to an end. Old Loyeff required a good deal more. Usually he got what he wanted.

"Now take this letter you just wrote and translate it into Hebrew."

Sholom did as he was told. In the end he was hired. Accompanied by the two Loyeffs, father and son, Sholom found himself inside another coach with fresh, spirited horses, the likes of which he had never seen. They started for the village of Sofievka, where the Loyeffs had their estate.

Riding in the coach, snugly wrapped in soft bearskins, Sholom recalled the wealthy merchants who used to pass him in large numbers on the way to the Yasnegradski inn; he felt as though he were one of them. He felt as though he were asleep, dreaming one of his rich dreams. There was something unreal about the events of the past few hours, the meeting with Joshua Loyeff after going to the synagogue, the friendship, the journey, the confrontation with the stern but obviously fair field marshal, and now the journey to their home. The events had the quality of one of orphan Shmulik's fantastic tales, which he had enjoyed so much as a boy.

It was night when they arrived. The sky was salted with stars. The coach halted in front of a baronial mansion. A guard ran to pry open the heavy gates. "Will I live here?" Sholom wondered, trembling involuntarily. It was not possible. They left the coach and started toward the house. Sholom walked as though in a trance. A servant appeared out of nowhere, opened the door noiselessly and bowed. Sholom stopped on the threshold, reluctant to go in. Someone gave him a gentle shove. He was aware of following his hosts, moving through a maze of rooms. The rooms were large, high-ceilinged and well-appointed. Servants darted in and out, like shadows. The only voice heard was Reb Elimelech Loyeff's.

Coming into a large, brilliantly-lighted room, Sholom saw a pretty girl of thirteen or fourteen. She sat on a couch next to her mother, a well-groomed, attractive woman, as you'd expect a field marshal's wife to be.

"This is Sholom Rabinowitz," Reb Elimelech said, "Olga's tutor."

Sholom made the proper salutations. Pleasantries were exchanged. They asked him about himself. His mind was in a whirl.

That night Shmulik came to him in his sleep. "I've found the hidden treasure," Sholom informed his friend.

Sofievka was paradise and he was determined to stay there. Not only must he make his mark as a tutor, Sholom decided; he must be on the alert to use the proper spoon, fork and knife at the table, to bear in mind not to make noises while eating. One had to be constantly on the alert. At home, he remembered, all the family ate out of one tureen, armed with large wooden spoons. Forks were used on occasion, but not knives. At home, if you lacked a spoon, you dipped a piece of *chaleh* (white twist bread) in the plate with the fingers God gave you. Here one had to have the brain of a prime minister to figure out what to do with all the silverware placed near you. He missed the informality of a simple Jewish home and sighed for the delights of a baked potato in its jacket, a few grains of sand on it. He longed for a slice of bread and herring.

But the moments of nostalgia were few. Soon they disappeared altogether. His job pleased him immensely. He was treated as one of the family. He taught Olga two or three hours daily, spending the rest of the time as he pleased, reading, writing and walking. He could not get enough of the outdoors, observing the trees, plants and grass like a blind man whose eyesight has been restored. The things that grew in the fields and meadows were filled with magic and mystery. All his life he had been a stranger to nature, although he lived near it. Like most Jewish boys growing up in the small towns of the Ukraine, he'd spent his waking hours inside the walls of a *cheder,* leaving the sun and God's green world to the Gentile boys. The wonders of growing

things revealed themselves to him now in all their splendor.

He treasured what he saw and learned. The mischievous boy of not long ago was being still further transformed into a sober, serious, inquiring man. His talent for mimicry found little outlet in Sofievka. Old Loyeff was too imposing a figure to arouse in Sholom a sense of the ridiculous. As for Olga, she became for him the fragile heroine of all the romantic novels he'd read, though he dared not admit it to himself. He and his pupil were inseparable companions.

His employer, Sholom quickly discovered, was not only wealthy, he was also an excellent farmer. Jewish farmers were rare in the Russia of those days. Jews were not encouraged to take their livelihood from the soil. After the repressive laws of 1882 came into effect, Jews were forbidden to own land altogether and were driven from the villages. Reb Elimelech was not an average farmer. He was an expert whom peasants as well as landowners consulted about farming. He was a cultivated man, well-read and well-versed in Hebrew as well as the Talmud. He owned a large library, the bulk of it in Hebrew, as Yiddish was not yet considered a language suited to literature.

Sholom spent many hours in Reb Elimelech's library. He read Shakespeare, Dickens, Tolstoi, Goethe, Gogol and many others. He also read lurid French novels and found time to write. He began timidly but found he wrote with ease. Words flowed effortlessly from his pen. As this was a period of

self-discovery as a writer, Sholom wrote whatever
came to mind: stories, novels, plays and sketches.
His novels, he later said, were heart-rending trage-
dies, for the most part. There appeared no plan in
the great outpouring. As soon as he had finished one
story, Sholom would carry it lovingly to Olga, his
audience and critic.

She read it eagerly. "It's a masterpiece, Sholom,"
Olga declared without any hesitation.

"You really like it, Olga?"

"Oh, this is the best thing you've done, by *far.*"

"I'm glad you think so," he said, supremely
happy. "I wasn't certain. I was too near the story
and couldn't view it objectively."

Several days later, thrusting a new one at Olga,
Sholom felt his pulse racing wildly. "I stayed up all
last night finishing it," he revealed.

Olga dropped all her work and read Sholom's
manuscript. "It's better than anything you've
done," she said. "There's no *comparison.*"

Sholom couldn't help agreeing. Reluctantly he
burned in the oven last week's "masterpiece." During the winter months, the oven consumed a dozen
novels and a score of dramas.

He knew now, beyond any doubt, that he would
be a writer. He had been wanting to be a writer for
many years. In Voronko, as a small boy, his imagination had been fired by a small book, old, slight, torn,
written in Yiddish. He did not recall the name of the
book. He remembered it with pleasure for its contents. His father would read from it every Sabbath
after sundown when many people gathered in their

home. One or two sentences was all that was required to start them laughing. Reb Nahum, unable
to contain himself, joined in the laughter. Sholom,
banished with the rest of the children to an adjacent
room, listened intently, a smile on his lips. His fondest wish was to grow up to be a writer of just such a
book, a book that brought laughter and joy to the
people who read it.

Now he tried putting laughter into some of his
stories, experimenting with humor. He also imitated
the tragedians. He was not in any hurry to find
himself as a writer, as old Loyeff took care of all his
material needs. It never occurred to Sholom that the
idyllic life might come to an abrupt end. Only one
cloud marred Sholom's sky: the army draft. Olga's
brother, Joshua, was immune from soldiering on account of a weak heart, which cost him his life several years later. But Sholom was physically fit. He
would be called any day.

Old Loyeff was irreconcilable. "Sholom-heart, we
must get you off," he said. "The Czar's army is no
place for a Jew, it's a sentence of death." Reb Elimelech, it appeared, was more concerned with Sholom's being called than the young tutor himself.

"If they call me I'll go," Sholom said, a note of
bravado in his voice. But as the day of induction
came near, he worried increasingly. His dreams of
making a name for himself in the Czar's army, he
knew all along, were absurd. Only in exceptional
cases was a Jew given the opportunity to rise to the
lowly rank of corporal or sergeant. Most Jews were

assigned menial tasks. Jews who went into the service as young men came out graybeards.

The day Sholom left to report was a dismal one in the Loyeff household. Olga stayed in her room, sobbing. Old Loyeff scolded the servants without any reason. Sholom left with heavy heart, realizing more poignantly than ever how deeply attached he was to the house, its owner, and particularly to Olga.

He left by coach, carrying with him a sealed envelope from his employer. The sky was shrouded in clouds. A sharp wind stole down from the north. Sholom cast a lingering look at the house. Would he see it again?

The letter old Loyeff gave him bulged in his breast pocket. "Hand it to the commander," Reb Elimelech had said. Sholom wondered what was in the letter. In what way could it be of help to him?

Arriving in the small town of Kaniev, Sholom went directly to headquarters and asked for the commander.

"Why do you want to see the commander?" one of the subordinates demanded.

Sholom replied: "I have a letter for him from Sofievka."

The commander appeared, a tall, mustachioed officer. Sholom held out the letter. "From Elimelech Loyeff," he said.

The commander took the letter and opened it. A smile appeared on his lips as he removed several large-denomination ruble notes from the envelope and stuffed them in his pocket. "Draw a number," he said to Sholom.

Sholom obeyed. He drew Number 285. In the evening, returning to headquarters, he saw on the bulletin board that the last number inducted into the army was 284!

His return to Sofievka proved a joyous occasion. Old Loyeff, who spent a fortune rescuing Sholom from the Czar's clutches, arranged a party. Sholom's head whirled from the happiness and the glass of wine he'd drunk. Olga looked very pretty, he thought. She looked no longer like a little girl; she was grown-up, womanly. After the party he summoned up the courage to tell her, "Being away from you was the worst thing."

"It was terrible," she said readily.

They vowed not to allow anything to come between them in the future.

11 The search

Aunt Toybe was not really an aunt. She was a distant relative of Reb Elimelech's, a wealthy widow from Berdichev who enjoyed spending the hot summer months in the country air. Her one distinction, so far as Sholom was concerned, was the informal manner she assumed with old Loyeff. She was the only person Sholom knew who was not afraid to argue with Reb Elimelech.

Sholom had little to do with Aunt Toybe. At the dinner table, where they met three times daily, she was always friendly and affable. He had no reason to suspect that she would unwittingly shatter his cozy little dream world. But one day, about half an hour before her departure for home, Aunt Toybe took Reb Elimelech aside and said to him, "Those two are in love."

"In love? Who's in love? What are you talking about?" he said, perplexed.

"I'm talking about Olga and her tutor," Aunt

Toybe explained. "They're crazy about each other."

Reb Elimelech threw his guest a withering glance. "Stop talking nonsense!" He conceived a sudden dislike for this chatterbox of a woman who did not know when to stop talking.

Aunt Toybe was not to be put off. "Anybody can see it," she said calmly, "who is not totally blind or unwilling to notice what is happening right under his nose. Don't you ever watch them during mealtimes, how they make eyes at each other?"

"Your coach is waiting!" Old Loyeff ended the conversation abruptly. He saw his guest leave, then went to his room. When dinner was served, Reb Elimelech was not in his accustomed place, at the head of the table. In the evening he summoned the family to his room. The servants, attuned to the unpredictable moods of their employer, talked in whispers.

On the following morning Olga did not come down for her customary walk with Sholom. He ate alone in the large deserted dining room. No one spoke to him. The servants avoided him.

"What's happening?" Sholom inquired, puzzled by their strange behavior toward him. Why hadn't Olga come down? Why were they all avoiding him? Had he done something wrong?

The servants stared at him with vacant eyes but said nothing. He felt blameless and yet there was no doubt in his mind about the finger of accusation pointing at him. Why? "I want to speak to the master," he declared.

The servants shook their heads and blocked his
path.

He demanded they let him speak to Olga. They
shook their heads.

All his attempts at seeing Reb Elimelech or Olga
proved fruitless. He haunted the living room, waiting for someone to appear. He waited in vain. The
Loyeffs did not come downstairs.

The house was like a tomb. The silence became
unbearable. Sholom went to his room and lay down
on the bed without undressing. He could not sleep.
Why were they avoiding him? He loved all of them
so dearly! Hard as he tried, he could not recall saying or doing anything to cause this violent change in
their attitude toward him. Why were they turning
on him? He could more readily accept the cold
sharp steel of an assassin's knife than this. The least
they might do was to state their reasons. Give a person the opportunity to defend himself.

He felt blameless. He regarded Olga as a "sister."
The thought that he might be in love with her,
Sholom dismissed as unworthy and profane.

In the morning, his eyes bloodshot from lack of
sleep, Sholom went downstairs, determined to seek
an explanation, come what may. "I want to speak to
the master!" he demanded.

"They're gone."

"Gone?" he cried out, shocked. He caught sight of
an envelope on the dining room table with his name
written on it. He recognized Reb Elimelech's sprawl-
ing handwriting. Sholom tore open the envelope, his
heart pounding. Perhaps he would find the answer

there. Several large-denomination bills fell out, and a note. The note contained two words: "Your salary." He searched frantically for a letter to explain once and for all why they were doing this to him. He found nothing. Tears stood in his eyes.

He pocketed the money without counting it and left the house. What a miserable ending, he thought, to three of the happiest years of my life——

A coachman drove him to the railroad station. "How can I get in touch with your master?" Sholom pleaded.

The coachman shrugged. "They don't tell me where they go."

"Stop at the post office," Sholom said.

At the post office Sholom jumped out of the sled and ran inside. The postmaster, Malinovski, was a friend of old Loyeff's. On more than one occasion Sholom had seen the two sitting down to a glass of tea or a measure of vodka.

Malinovski greeted the young tutor as though they were old friends. He ushered him into his private office, uncorked a bottle of vodka and insisted they drink to their "friendship."

Sholom, manfully holding back tears, told Malinovski what had happened at Sofievka. It struck him even while he was talking that the man was not really interested. But he *had* to tell someone.

Malinovski, primed by several drinks, listened attentively, nodded sympathetically and urged Sholom to take another drink.

Distraught, Sholom reached for another drink.

"Would you do me a favor?" he cried, as Malinovski raised his tumbler to drink his guest's health.

"Of course! Anything you desire, my friend!"

"Would you give a letter of mine to Olga Loyeff?" He had written the letter before leaving the house in Sofievka.

Malinovski nodded. "It's the least you can ask of a friend!" he exclaimed. "I'll give it to her personally."

"Thank you, thank you." Tears stood in his eyes.

Sholom left his "friend," considerably relieved. Olga would read his letter and answer; yes, she would answer. How could she do otherwise?

At the railroad station he said goodbye to Loyeff's coachman and got on the train. He found a seat and collapsed in it. Where was he going? Not back to Pereyaslav; it had nothing to offer him. All his friends had left the town. He missed only his father. "Why not go to Kiev?" he thought. Wasn't it about time he struck out on his own? His pocket was filled with money. He had not bothered counting how much he had, but it must be a sizeable amount, his salary for three years.

Kiev drew him powerfully. The Ukraine's largest city, it was also one of its most beautiful. For Sholom the city had another strong attraction: Kiev was where many Jewish novelists, poets and essayists lived. It was from there that much of the new Hebrew literature came. In Sholom's reveries, the city was filled with artists of the pen whom he considered "luminous stars in the heavens." There he would go, to sit at the feet of the great, to worship

and pay homage and hope some of their brilliance
would rub off and adhere to him.

But Kiev presented insurmountable problems to
a young man of twenty, without any skills and lacking a residence permit required of Jews. The only
Jews allowed to live in Kiev were those who had the
means to bribe officials, skilled artisans, veterans of
the Czar's army, and parents whose children attended the Gymnasia. The Jewish population of the
city was confined, for the most part, to Kiev's worst
slum, the Podol. There Jews dwelt in hunger and
misery, their ranks swelling by the arrival of thousands from the small towns and villages where they
could not earn a livelihood. Lacking residence per-
mits, many of them hid in cellars and attics during
police raids. After the police had gone, they came
out. Thousands of Jews lived in this fashion, fugi-
tives, keeping one step ahead of the police. Those
caught were sent back to the congested little towns
whence they came. Notwithstanding the obstacles
flung in their path, Jews became doctors, architects,
lawyers, engineers and merchants. There were even
a few who attained great wealth.

Sholom's mind was made up. Others had tried
Kiev and gained a foothold and stayed in the city.
What had he to lose?

He arrived in the great city toward evening. Kiev
struck him as a huge cauldron, boiling and seething.
The people flung themselves about like chickens in
the slaughterhouse. But what he found most difficult to comprehend was the complete indifference
people displayed toward him. It seemed to Sholom

that not one person in a thousand bothered taking notice of his arrival.

After many inquiries and false starts, Sholom found a room in the Podol. He closed the door and sat down to write to Olga. (He wrote again on the following day and every day. After several weeks, Sholom wondered why Olga did not answer. It did not occur to him that the letters he sent to Malinovski and meant for Olga were turned over by the postmaster to her father, Reb Elimelech, who read and destroyed them.) Finishing the letter, Sholom went to the manager of the inn and asked where he could find a mailbox.

The manager, an old man with rheumy eyes, looked at his young guest searchingly and asked him what he was doing in Kiev.

Sholom shrugged and gave an evasive reply. He did not like the man's probing.

Perhaps Sholom wanted a job, the man inquired.

"Perhaps, and perhaps not," Sholom responded. The old man gave up in disgust.

As though to test his resolve, the police raided the inn in which Sholom was staying and he spent his first night in Kiev freezing in a tiny attic, along with a score of guests. Undaunted, his eyes full of sleep, he got up in the morning, determined to see the poet I. L. Levin, whom he held in great esteem.

The poet worked in the great sugar factory owned by the wealthy Jew, Brodsky. Levin, who wrote in Hebrew, labored in the basement of the factory, in a tiny damp office, keeping books. Sholom had little difficulty finding the Brodsky factory. Everyone

knew of Brodsky, not only in Kiev, but in the rest of
the Ukraine. But who ever heard of Levin? Only
those who loved poetry and read Hebrew. And yet,
Sholom found him. After many hours of searching.
He went down into the basement of the Brodsky
enterprise with a fluttering heart and sweating
palms. Near Levin's office, he stopped momentarily,
then went inside. The poet, a fat little man, was
pacing the measure of a room, both hands folded
on his chest. He must be composing a new poem,
Sholom thought reverently. Should he announce his
presence? Should he say hello? Perhaps he should
clear his throat and announce his presence, since
Levin walked right past him without taking notice
of him. Sholom hesitated. If he interrupted the
poet's creative labors, a gem might be lost to the
world. He decided to wait. Finally he cleared his
throat. Levin continued pacing, taking no notice of
the visitor.

"Hello," Sholom blurted out. His knees were
weak.

Levin stopped briefly, threw Sholom a cold, cross-
eyed look and resumed pacing.

Sholom, who had hoped he would be asked to sit
down, was not discouraged. This must be the way of
great poets, he reasoned. Lord Byron would not
have acted differently! Why should Levin greet him
in a friendly manner? Who am I? he asked himself. A nobody, compared with the poet! Nonetheless
he felt like an imbecile standing there, not knowing
what to do with his hands, terrified he would say

something that might be misinterpreted or misunderstood.

"Goodbye," Sholom said, fleeing down the empty corridor.

Each morning he ventured out to storm the battlements of Kiev. He rang the bells of influential people. He ran to the *rabbiner,* the government rabbi, and pleaded for help in obtaining a residence permit. Everywhere he was met with hostile glances and indifference. He watched in consternation as his money dwindled. One morning he woke with not enough money to pay next week's rent for his room. Now, he knew, it was time to leave.

Despondent, Sholom wrote his father: "Send money for train fare. I am returning to Pereyaslav."

The money arrived by return mail and with a letter from his father, written in Hebrew, informing Sholom that in the town of Luben, not far from Pereyaslav, an election would soon be held for a new *rabbiner.* He begged Sholom to hurry to Luben and announce his candidacy for the post. In conclusion Reb Nahum informed his son that Uncle Pinney was writing a letter to one of Luben's most influential citizens on Sholom's behalf and when Sholom arrived in Luben, he should see the man and he would help him a great deal.

Reb Nahum's faith in his son was unwavering. But his enthusiasm was not contagious. Sholom pocketed the money and Uncle Pinney's letter of introduction and set out for Luben. Several years ago, the prospect of a position as a *rabbiner* would have filled him with enthusiasm. At one time he had planned to study for *rabbiner*. However, in Sofievka his energies had flowed in another direction, writing. Writing was what he wished to do, even now. But it was all-important that he begin earning money without any delay. Reluctantly he got on the train for Luben.

Sholom knew that *rabbiners,* forced on the Jews by the Czarist government, were not always held in high esteem by the people. The Jews preferred their own rabbis. However, there was one thing to be said for the institution of *rabbiner:* he was chosen through fair elections in which all the Jews of the community could participate, if they wished. A well-paying post, it was eagerly sought. The campaigns were usually stormy. Opposing candidates (there could be more than two) called one another names; there were bitter accusations. By election time, the town was in an uproar. The tumult sometimes continued long after the election, when losing candidates ran to the state capital to plead with the government for a recount of the votes or for a new election, claiming they had been cheated. Sholom knew all this could and did happen. He was also aware that in Luben he would be resented as a stranger seeking to deprive one of their own people of a good job. Furthermore, his extreme youth (for a *rabbiner*) would be held against him. He was barely twenty-one.

He arrived in the strange town in the morning and went to the home of one of Luben's richest Jews,

Reb Nahman. There he presented Uncle Pinney's letter.

Reb Nahman, well along in years, was Luben's most respected citizen. So powerful was he that prayers in the synagogue usually did not begin until Reb Nahman arrived. But as he was quite old and infirm, Reb Nahman could not always manage to come on time. On such occasions the congregation waited. It waited, even though Reb Nahman had sent a messenger ahead with word to proceed with the prayers because he would be late. But the congregation waited anyway. So important a man was old Reb Nahman!

Sholom was let in by a servant. Several minutes later he was ushered into Reb Nahman's august presence. Reb Nahman took the letter but did not ask his guest to sit. He read slowly, finished, cleared his throat and finally took notice of his young visitor. He put on his glasses the better to see Sholom. "Let me hear you talk," he imperiously commanded.

Sholom shrugged, opened his mouth and began talking. From earthly matters, Sholom went on to the Talmud. The old man permitted himself a smile. "Sit down," he said to Sholom. To a servant he said, "Bring refreshments."

Not many hours later, a rumor spread like a brush-fire that a brand new candidate for *rabbiner* had arrived in town. Although very young, the new candidate was said to possess all the virtues. In the first place, he was said to be a relative of Reb Nahman's. As for his knowledge of the Bible, it was phenomenal. The rumor grew to fantastic proportions.

Before evening prayer all of Luben knew that the
new candidate was a veritable King Solomon, so wise
was he in the matter of solving disputes. Appearing
on the street, Sholom was aware of fingers pointing
at him, of people staring at him and talking about
him.

There were exclamations of surprise, cries of astonishment; some declared he was too young, his
mother's milk had not dried on his lips; some said his
hair was too long. . . . What a *likely* candidate!

Sholom threw himself into the campaign with an
energy born of desperation. He visited all of the
town's distinguished citizens and dazzled them with
his knowledge of the Talmud and Hebrew. In the
synagogue, called before the Ark, he made them
gasp at the flawless manner in which he executed his
prayer. But it was on the day of election that
Sholom truly scaled the heights. Standing on the
podium of the town's only hall, Sholom, who followed his two opponents, delivered himself of an
oration that made the voters shout "Hurrah!" He
began his speech in perfect Russian, skipped nimbly
on to Hebrew, then Yiddish. He glided effortlessly
from one language to another, quoting the Bible
when he saw fit. His linguistic acrobatics took the
electorate by storm. But he did not neglect to make
his speech in the form of a tale, one that made them
laugh. In the end, he was chosen by acclamation.

The election over, the new *rabbiner* went to Reb
Nahman's home to thank him for his help. Reb
Nahman was moved. He asked Sholom to repeat the

speech he'd made at the hall. It must have been very good to create such a sensation, he said.

"How good it was you will have to judge for yourself, Reb Nahman."

"Let's hear." Reb Nahman put on his glasses and Sholom repeated the tale he'd told the voters.

The story Sholom told them dealt with, of all things, a priest, a young priest just emerging from the needle, as they say. This young priest one day came to his superior, the Metropolitan, to be blessed and to inquire what he should talk about for his first sermon in the church. The Metropolitan suggested that the young priest tell his parishioners about the miracles witnessed by the holy; for instance, the miracle that occurred to the forty holy men who were lost for three days and three nights in the forest and almost perished from hunger. But God performed one of his miracles and the holy men found bread. All forty of them sat down and shared the one loaf. They ate and they ate and they ate . . . and there was enough bread left over for the morrow. . . . On the following Sunday, the young priest stood up before his congregation to deliver the sermon. But suffering from stage fright, he altered the story just a little bit. Once a holy man, he told them, lost his way in the forest. He wandered around for three days and three nights and almost perished from hunger. But God performed one of his miracles and the holy man found forty loaves of bread. He sat down to eat and he ate and he ate and he ate . . . and there was enough bread left over for the morrow. . . . Later in the day, the Metropolitan scolded the young priest for making such a grievous error. But the young priest defended himself, arguing that for his parishioners this too was a miracle.

"So you won by making them laugh," Reb Nahman observed, pleased. The host might have added that the new *rabbiner*, in addition to making them laugh, had also told them a story. In later years his genius for provoking laughter went hand in hand with storytelling.

As a *rabbiner*, Sholom left little to be desired. Notwithstanding his extreme youth, he gained a reputation among the people of Luben as a wise and compassionate public servant. He held the post for three years and might have kept it indefinitely had not something extraordinary happened.

One day a visitor was announced. Sholom went out to meet him. "Reb Loyeff!" he cried. And indeed, before him stood the tall, majestic Reb Elimelech Loyeff, a friendly smile on his lips.

"I came to speak with you, Sholom-heart," he said in as contrite a tone of voice as it is possible for a field marshal to summon. "I want you to come back to Sofievka."

12 Sholom Aleichem

Sholom's marriage to Olga Loyeff was a glittering affair. Only now was Sholom able to piece together the puzzling behavior of his father-in-law during those unhappy days three years ago. He discovered that old Loyeff's objections to their romance were caused by his ignorance of it. Why wasn't he consulted? How dared they, or anyone else, do things in Reb Elimelech's house without obtaining his permission? He did not object if his daughter married a "pauper," so long as the young man was worthy. But that she should make her own selection, instead of letting *him* do it, this he refused to accept. Reb Elimelech considered himself a "modern" man. He did not hold that the only way one found a suitable husband for a daughter was to call in professional matchmakers. He had planned personally to make the selection of a husband for his only daughter. In his estimation, Olga deserved the best. Olga's mind was quite made up that Sholom was the best, the finest and noblest. No amount of reasoning and cajoling altered her opinion. Having a will of her own, she rejected all suitors who came to the great house in Sofievka. It would be Sholom or nobody, she declared. In the end the father gave in. He embraced Sholom as a son and he did it with a full heart.

After marrying Olga, Sholom managed the estate of his father-in-law. Although very busy, he found time to write. Reb Elimelech died in 1885, two years after his daughter's marriage. Sholom and Olga moved to Kiev. This time he experienced no difficulty in obtaining a residence permit in the city, as they were rich, his wife having inherited a quarter of a million rubles.

In Kiev, he became involved in matters that had little relation to literature. As a speculator on the stock exchange, he was up to his neck in stocks, bonds, bulls and bears, investing thousands of rubles, buying, selling. He came home exhausted. Unable to sleep, he began writing. He wrote what came to mind. His thoughts wandered back to what now appeared as the carefree days of his boyhood. "The Penknife," one of his best stories, was the result of these nocturnal outpourings; it dramatized the ordeal of a boy who steals a penknife and suffers guilt pangs as a result. The story, thinly disguised as fiction, was based on a harrowing experience Sholom had as a boy. It had happened in Pereyaslav, during their innkeeping days. Sholom, who had discovered the charms of music, was determined to become a violinist. But he lacked the money to buy an instrument. Where was he to obtain the money? To ask his father for the money was out of the question; his father was not earning enough. Sholom searched desperately for an answer. He ran errands for the guests at the inn, waited on them, brought the samovar to them, shined shoes. But the tips he got and saved were not nearly enough to buy a violin. And yet, he could not live without a violin! It was the one thing in life that *mattered*.

There was only one person from whom money could be obtained, from a guest called Wolfson, a rich wheat merchant. So wealthy was Wolfson, his room was held vacant and ready for him even when he was away from Pereyaslav! It was known as Wolfson's room. He rated his own samovar, known as Wolfson's samovar. Nobody drank tea from it save Wolfson. He was on intimate terms with the household and behaved as one of the family. He smoked thick cigars and was fond of talking incessantly, chewing on his cigar, his hands deep in his pockets. The door to his room was usually open. The desk drawer was locked, but the keys hung nearby. One turn of the key and the drawer opened. What was inside the drawer, everybody in the house knew. It was filled with money! The money was kept in a thick wallet. There was, in addition, an old leather purse, bulging with change, silver coins and copper ones. Sholom had no doubt that if he owned half the money in the leather purse alone, he could buy the best violin in the world.

Quite often Wolfson opened the drawer in the presence of a number of people and Sholom caught sight—against his will, as it was a sin to covet what belonged to another—of the bulging wallet and the purse filled with coins. His fondest wish was for Wolfson to lose the purse and for himself to find it. But Wolfson appeared in no hurry to lose it. Another notion was born in Sholom's fertile mind: Wolfson might one day give him his trousers to be pressed, forgetting to remove the change purse. Sholom would contrive to let the purse slide out of the trouser pocket, and that would be that. He would pick it up, put it in his own pocket and simply forget to return it to its owner. One could not call that stealing. Wolfson, however, had a nasty habit of emptying his pockets before giving his clothes to Sholom to be cleaned.

Sholom decided on a desperate move. He would go into Wolfson's room, open the drawer, take out the purse and look inside it to find out how much money it contained. He would not steal and commit a sin, he would merely look.

One morning he did it! He went into Wolfson's room, pretending he was tidying it up. Wolfson was in the living room, smoking a thick cigar and talking. Sholom seized the keys. Suddenly he retreated as if stung. It seemed to him the keys made a frightful noise, alerting the whole world to the deed he was about to commit. His limbs trembling, Sholom fled.

He tried again several days later. Wolfson, who disliked staying alone in his room, preferring the small living room where the guests gathered to talk, went out and left the door open, as usual. Sholom went in. He sprang at the desk, seized the keys, inserted the proper one in the keyhole and turned. The lock responded. The drawer flew open. He stared inside the drawer and a shiver ran down his spine. The wallet was there, at the very top, bursting with money. Pull out one note, just one, and you're the owner of a violin! he thought. Take it, fool! Pull it out! Who will ever know? His feverish brain urged him on, but his hands refused to obey. His hands began to tremble. His teeth chattered. His eyes wandered from the wallet to the little old leather purse filled with coins. He reached for the purse but quickly withdrew. His hands seemed paralyzed. Grab it! put it in your pocket! What are you waiting for? Suddenly he heard the unmistakable sound of Wolfson's house slippers shuffling in the hallway. He shut the drawer, turned the key and left. Out in the hall, he found nobody. Thief . . . idiot! he berated himself.

On his third try, Sholom did not falter. Reconciled with the notion that he was a thief, the boy went into Wolfson's room, opened the drawer, seized the small leather purse, shoved it in his pocket, locked the drawer and went to school. He did all of this deliberately, without hurrying, as though he were an expert at stealing. His calmness deserted him as soon as he left the inn. The small purse was like a burning coal against his flesh. He would never get all the way to school. He would not survive the day with that burning object in his pocket. He changed his course abruptly and went inside the shed, a small, dark place filled with kindling wood. A damp smell permeated the shed. He bent down, crawled to a corner and hid the purse near the wall, beneath a pile of wood. He retraced his steps and started for school.

As he made his way along the street, Sholom was certain that all who saw him knew him for what he was, a thief. His eyes betrayed him, his walk, his manner. Guilt was written all over him.

In the classroom he went quietly to his seat. He could not concentrate on the work. His mind was elsewhere, in the shed. Suddenly he realized that in his excitement he had failed to open the purse and examine its contents.

Like a sleepwalker, he floated from one classroom to the next. Classes dragged on interminably. He thought school would never come to an end. With the ringing of the bell Sholom was on his feet. Ignoring his friend Ali, who wanted to talk with him, Sholom ran home. The shed was his destination. He must find out the contents of the purse. Nothing else mattered.

Entering the house, Sholom was greeted by a frightful scene. The place looked as though it had been struck by a tornado. The bedding was off the beds, piled on the floor. The furniture had been moved. Tables were turned over, chairs stacked. The kitchen was unrecognizable. The maid, a young peasant woman, was weeping, claiming she did not take the purse. Sholom's stepmother flung curses in all directions, crying the purse had been taken right from under the nose. A purse filled with money has been swallowed by the earth, may the earth swallow all of them! Nobody's seen the purse, may they not see the world!

The whole family was busy searching, turning the house upside down. Even some of the guests joined in. The least concerned appeared the victim himself, Wolfson. He stood calmly to one side, smoking a thick cigar, hands deep in his pockets, an enigmatic smile on his lips. He had it in the morning, he said in an even tone of voice, and he hadn't been out of the house.

Reb Nahum, his brow a maze of wrinkles, sighed and maintained that the purse must be somewhere in the house. He turned to his silent brood of children, a note of supplication in his voice, and asked if anyone of them had seen it.

A dozen blank faces greeted Reb Nahum's query. Then Sholom stepped forward. "Seen what?" he asked with an air of innocence.

Reb Nahum flew into a rage. Turning on his favorite son, he cried that all morning they were going out of their minds trying to find Reb Wolfson's purse, turning the house upside down, and now he comes in and asks a question like that! He finished, wiped the perspiration from his forehead, turned to Reb Wolfson and asked in a tone of voice he tried hard to control how much money there was in the purse.

Wolfson shrugged and, smiling as though amused, said that the purse itself mattered. This very morning he had had it. He hadn't left the house, not for a minute.

Sholom saw his father's ashen face, a mask of misery. His conscience was further torn when the maid was told to go home and not come back. "I don't want a thief working for me," the stepmother said to the peasant girl. The maid left, protesting her innocence. Sholom listened to the poor girl's sobs and his heart shrank. What a mess you've managed to make! he thought to himself. What a terrible mess!

Were it possible to erase the deed, he would gladly do it. But it was too late. What now?

The shed drew him but Sholom dared not leave the house. The tumult subsided toward evening. He left quietly and came out into the dark courtyard. He went into the shed, crept toward the corner where he had hidden the purse and found it. Now he would see what was in it. His breath coming in short gasps, Sholom opened it. And there before him lay one solitary coin, an old worthless coin, its face worn smooth by time and handling. "Idiot, thief," he said, disgusted with himself. Not only would this fail to purchase a violin, it would not even be taken in exchange for a piece of hard candy. The terrible ordeal had been for nothing. . . .

At night he could not fall asleep. And yet at times it occurred to him that he was asleep and having a nightmare. It *must* be a nightmare, he thought. He was *not* a thief. It could not be. A cold sweat bathed his body. How low one can descend, he thought. You're a common ordinary thief—he hated himself. And he hated Wolfson no less. Earlier in the evening, his stepmother sent him to Wolfson's room with the samovar. "What's new?" Wolfson had asked, a smile on his lips. Had the purse been found?

The question and the smile convinced Sholom that Wolfson knew who had stolen the purse, as well as how the thief felt, finding nothing but a worthless coin in it. Wolfson knew and was amused. And Sholom hated him for it, with all his being.

He fell asleep and dreamed of old purses and faceless coins. He woke up with a scream. Something must be done about the purse . . . he must get rid of it without delay . . . the evidence must be destroyed. Bury it. But where? Should he toss it over the Christian neighbor's fence? Perhaps he should drop it in the crowded cemetery? No, the river would be the best place, drop it in the water. He decided on the river as the best choice. . . .

Sholom counted the days until the Sabbath, when he would be free from classes. On the fateful day he got up early, dressed and accompanied his father to the synagogue. In the afternoon he ran back to the shed, seized the worthless purse and put it in his pocket. He started for the little wooden bridge crossing the river. It was crowded with strollers, among them his friends. Boys called to him; he replied curtly to their greetings but did not stop. The purse was a heavy stone in his pocket. The water drew him. He ran. Finding a deserted stretch of riverbank, he stopped, out of breath, lowered his hand into his pocket and took out the purse. He gazed at it momentarily, grimacing as though in pain. The ugly old purse was like a living thing in his hand, the touch of it soiling him. Suddenly he flung it from him. An instant later he heard a plop in the water, saw a large ring. Then it was quiet, his crime buried in a watery grave.

In story form, the painful boyhood experience with the worthless purse emerged as "The Penknife." He completed the tale in a short time and sent it off to a magazine and thought no more about it. His mind was too preoccupied with money matters and the stock market to worry about the fate of a short story. One day he opened the pages of a magazine and was surprised to find a review of his story. He read, his blood racing. The well-known critic Dubnow praised the tale as an outstanding achievement. The young author, Dubnow declared, possessed talent. There wasn't any doubt that he would one day help enrich our impoverished Yiddish literature.

He read the lines and tears were in his eyes. His feeling of gratitude to Dubnow never left him. He recalled the critic's encouraging lines even after he became a writer of world prominence. What would Dubnow say about this one? he asked himself each time he completed a story.

"The Penknife" was written in Yiddish. During Sholom's Sofievka writing days, before his marriage, he worked with the Russian and Hebrew languages. Yiddish was not considered a language for literary expression. Only one author dared write in Yiddish, Mendele Mocher Sforim. He was a great writer and therefore his voice was heard. Mendele's logic appeared simple. In view of the fact that the great majority of Jews spoke Yiddish, they could best be reached by literature written in that language. Moreover, Yiddish was a warm, expressive language,

perfectly suited to literature. Sholom had read Mendele and idolized him. No doubt the great writer's
courageous trail-blazing was not lost on Sholom. According to his own account, he began writing in
Yiddish because his literary efforts in Hebrew and
Russian piled up in editors' wastebaskets. In view of
the fact that the Russian and Hebrew publications
refused to print his stories and novels, he decided, as
a lark, to write something in Yiddish. He was pleas-
antly surprised when the publication not only pub-
lished what he sent but asked for more. The publication was called *Folksblatt,* and had the distinction of
being the first newspaper to appear in Yiddish.

Folksblatt began printing Sholom Aleichem's stories regularly. But he did not consider his writing as
anything but a diversion, a plaything. He signed his
tales Sholom Aleichem, a name he chose to disguise
his real one, not wishing his colleagues at the Stock
Exchange to know he dabbled in writing.

The publication of ''The Penknife'' caused a revolution in his life. If in the past there had been
qualms as to whether he was a businessman or a
writer, these increased a hundredfold after the publication of the story. Writing ceased being a plaything. He would make Yiddish his working language.

In a short time the name Sholom Aleichem was a
household word. He wrote in the everyday language
of the people. He captured this living, breathing,
vital language in its fullness and put it in his stories.
Reading his tales, people heard themselves talk.
They recognized their own voices and those of their

neighbors. "It is me he's talking about!" they exclaimed in wonder.

He wrote about their daily problems, their joys and sorrows and small triumphs. His stories ridiculed their enemies, who were many, and satirized the rich and the pretentious. The poor he encouraged to take pride in themselves, to know their worth, to remain faithful to themselves and to their rich heritage as Jews.

He became a legend while he was still alive. His tales delighted millions of readers. No writer captured the idiom with such fidelity, before or after him, although a number of literary giants crossed the Yiddish literary scene. Nor was there another writer with his ability to bring laughter into the drab lives of the ghetto dwellers. His name was linked with the great writers, with Dickens, Mark Twain and Gogol. Tolstoi, Chekhov and Gorki praised his work.

In 1888 he founded a Yiddish magazine, *Die Yiddishe Folksbibliotek*. To attract authors of distinction and talent, he paid large fees for contributions, an unheard-of thing, as most writers received little or nothing for their literary efforts. He delighted in finding new talent and aiding it. New authors beat down his doors to read him their works. He rarely turned them away. Sometimes listening was painful in the extreme, but when he discovered a new talent, Sholom Aleichem was overjoyed.

As was inevitable, the house of cards he erected toppled, and he found himself without money, having lost it on the Stock Exchange. Relieved of the

money, it seemed less difficult to make the inevitable
choice, that of becoming a writer every waking hour
of the day. Now he would devote *all* his time to
writing.

The question arose as to where he should do his
work. "What do you think of going to Odessa?" he
said to Olga and the children. The climate in Odessa
was pleasant and there was the Black Sea in which
to bathe. The city had an additional virtue: Mendele
Mocher Sforim lived there.

Mendele, whom Sholom Aleichem in later years
nicknamed "Grandpa," was the acknowledged master among Jewish writers. Born Sholom Jacob Abra-
mowitz in Kopel, Lithuania, in 1836 or 1837, his early
writing was in the Hebrew language. In 1864 he
struck out on a new path, adopting Yiddish as a me-
dium of literary expression. His excellent portraits
of ghetto dwellers established him as a writer of the
first rank.

Mendele exerted a powerful influence on Sholom
Aleichem. His advice, which the younger man eagerly sought, was always direct and to the point.
One afternoon "Grandpa" dropped in at Sholom
Aleichem's Odessa home. The host invited his illustrious guest to sit in the best chair. After Mendele
had sat down he fussed over him as though he were
a fragile object on the point of breaking. "Are you
comfortable, Grandpa?" he asked over and over
again.

"I'm fine," Mendele replied, amused. "Stop both-
ering yourself about me and instead let me hear what
you've written lately."

Sholom Aleichem, who had been waiting for his visitor to inquire about his latest work, nodded eagerly. "I do have something new," he confessed, "a novel."

"A novel?" Mendele was surprised. He had come to expect short stories, sketches and monologues from his gifted young friend. "What kind of a novel is it?"

"A serious novel," Sholom Aleichem confessed.

Mendele puckered his lips. "The great humorist has written a serious novel, eh? Well, let us see it."

The host brought his manuscript and deposited it lovingly in Mendele's lap and retreated to sit quietly, waiting for the verdict.

Mendele, adjusting his spectacles, read. After a brief lapse of time he lifted his eyes from a page he was reading, sighed and asked if there was a fire burning in the oven.

The host replied in the affirmative. A fire was burning and a meal was being cooked.

Mendele handed Sholom Aleichem his manuscript and told him to throw it in the fire. "Leave romance to others," he said "Stick to humor."

Sholom Aleichem, who had a formidable reputation at the time, might have rejected the master's words. But he chose the wiser course, he took the advice.

In 1892 he began writing one of his most memorable books, *Menachem Mendl.*

Menachem Mendl was a man as well as a type, found all too frequently in the restricted areas where Jews were allowed to live. Menachem Mendl was known as a *luftmensch,* one who tried coaxing a livelihood out of the air, one who tried making something out of nothing. A *luftmensch* possessed no skill, was not allowed to own land, was not allowed to live in the large cities. How was he to feed, clothe and house his wife and children?

Menachem Mendl had a wife, Sheine-Sheindl, and a brood of children. All of them were starving until one day Sheine-Sheindl was notified that a small inheritance was waiting for her in the faraway city of Kishinev. Menachem Mendl set out to collect it. On the way back, he decided to stop briefly in Odessa and try his luck on the Stock Market. There was no doubt in his mind that the small number of rubles in his pocket would be parlayed into a fortune. In his first letter to his wife (the book is an exchange of letters), Menachem Mendl is bubbling with enthusiasm. He could not begin to describe Odessa, he writes, its vastness and beauty, its wonderful people, its extraordinary business opportunities. There he was, strolling down the street, cane in hand. The sun was shining, the street jammed with people, trading, doing business in twenty thousand different items. If his heart desired to deal in wheat, he could have that. If he wanted to bid for corn, it's corn, or wool, flour, feathers, raisins, herring. . . . Whatever the lips can utter, one will find here in Odessa.

Sheine-Sheindl, who was glad to hear from her husband—she'd thought he got lost somewhere on his way back from Kishinev—wrote back letting him know that they were, thank God, in the best of health. The spasms which used to plague her had come back, she added. About his Odessa enterprise, she had an ominous feeling he would lose what little money was left them. . . . His saying that he was, thank God, earning money was welcome news. But what bothered her was this: having taken the trouble to write, why didn't he write so a person could understand what he was talking about? Why didn't he tell them *what* he was selling? How much was it by the yard? Or maybe it was sold by the pound? What further baffled her was his saying that the "object" he bought recently had risen in price. . . . If that's so, why didn't he sell it, the fool? What was he waiting for? She advised him to sell the "objects," the sooner the better, and to come home with what little money he had left.

This was only the first exchange of letters between them. Menachem Mendl's brain was bursting with plans. But Sheine-Sheindl, who was married to him for many years, knew better. She knew nothing would come of it.

After losing money on the Stock Market, Menachem Mendl became an agent, a writer, a marriage broker. From Odessa he fled to Kiev, to Warsaw, to Petrograd.

As a person, Menachem Mendl was not a fool. But his judgment was impaired by living too long on a merry-go-round that failed to stop. He was Sholom Aleichem's most tragic character. But reading his misadventures called forth no tears; instead, the ghetto shook with laughter. How could one not laugh at a marriage broker who was so eager to make a match and earn a commission that by mis-

take he brought together two people of the same
sex!

Like his fictional character, Sholom Aleichem too
left Odessa because he could not make a living
there. He was unhappy to part with Mendele and his
many friends, among them some of the outstanding
Jewish writers in Russia. But his literary efforts,
successful though they were artistically, failed to
provide for a family of eight. He returned to Kiev.
He had no intention of giving up writing. He was
more immersed in his writing than ever. He was in
love with his people and their literature. Yiddish
literature was extraordinarily beautiful! But the
true hard fact was that not even one Yiddish writer
earned a living by his pen.

He returned to Kiev, his mind alive with business
schemes. Cane in hand, he went back to the Stock
Market, to the brokerage houses, to the old associ-
ates far removed from the world of writing and the
things that had become as dear to him as life itself.
He was a man divided, cleaved in two, by the harsh
necessities of life itself. But he forsook business finally and irrevocably in 1900, admitting failure.
Henceforth he would be a professional writer in Yiddish.

He did not decide this lightly. What made the
burden less staggering was his family's enthusiastic
approval.

He plunged into his work with renewed vigor. He
was forever making notes in his neat hand, filling
one little notebook after another. His ear was like an
unfailing antenna, attuned to the sorrows as well as

the joys of his people. Completing a piece of writing, he summoned his wife and children. "I have written something new."

"Papa has written something new, hurrah!"

"Let's hear!"

As he read, he portrayed each character, employing gesture, inflection and pitch of voice. His gift for mimicry came into full play; he was Menachem Mendl and Scheine-Sheindl and a host of other characters. He delighted in impersonating people, his own fictional people as well as those who came to visit. The family laughed uproariously. They clapped and shouted "Bravo!" On such occasions, Sholom Aleichem was a happy man, because he heard laughter.

In 1901 there began to appear tales about the town of Voronko, which he named Kasrilovka. The Town of the Little People, he called it, bringing to life an astonishing number of characters, young as well as old, some of whom he had known at one time or another, many of them invented. Tucked away in a corner of the Ukraine, removed from the world— he wrote in an introduction—there stood little Kasrilovka. For the people of Kasrilovka such words as automobile and aviation had absolutely no meaning. For quite a long time they even rejected any notion of a railroad, refusing to believe reports that railroads existed altogether. "Nonsense," they cried. "Poppycock." Until, one day a Kasrilovka man was forced by a business commitment to go to Moscow. On his return, the man swore by all that was holy that he, personally, had ridden a train. Of course the people of Kasrilovka, who knew better, didn't believe a word he said. "How can a respectable Jew tell such a bald-faced lie?" they asked one another.

But he maintained stubbornly that he had been on the train; he would show them what it looked like, he went on, determined to convince the skeptics. He asked for a pencil and paper and drew for them a sketch of a train, how the wheels turn, the chimney whistles and the cars fly. The little people heard him out, shook their heads knowingly, as though convinced, but laughed inwardly, to themselves.

There was no fooling the Kasriels. They were poor—poor but merry, always ready for a good time. They were an exceptional breed of men who, although they did not delight in their pauperdom, wore it as though it were a medal to be redeemed for eternal happiness when they reached paradise. That the poor were destined for paradise, this the Kasriels and Sholom Aleichem firmly believed. The fact that life on earth was something less than the Garden of Eden did not dampen their spirits. You might inquire of them how they made a living, for it is obvious to you that they have no visible means of support. In response to your question they chuckle and point to themselves as proof they're alive and kicking. Observe them as they scurry about like headless chickens, hither and thither; they haven't a minute to spare. They appear to be running for the exercise itself. But if you can stop one of them, he will tell you that the Sabbath is near and the Kasriels who have nothing to eat are running around trying to earn a few pennies for the holiday.

As Sholom Aleichem conceived them, the Kasriels toiled all week long to make it possible for them to observe the Sabbath in the time-honored manner. And truly, with the arrival of the lovely Sabbath, they had no equals. There was always something to be found on a Jewish table, a fish, perhaps a slice of meat, or if not, a herring or an onion with bread. Lacking food, one borrowed from a neighbor; next week the neighbor would borrow from him.

Sholom Aleichem tells a story about a Kasriel who, determineod to starve no longer, leaves town and becomes a wanderer in the world. Arriving in Paris, he decides to seek an audience with the fabulously wealthy Rothschild. For what good is being in Paris without having a chat with Rothschild? There appears only one obstacle: he can't get in to see Rothschild; the guard at Rothschild's door tells him his clothes are in tatters. If his clothes were whole, he replies indignantly, he would not have left Kasrilovka to come to Paris. Things do not look bright, but a Kasrilovka Jew never says die. He finds a way out. He turns to the obstinate guard and tells him to inform his master that the visitor has brought with him a priceless item that cannot be bought in Paris.

Rothschild orders the visitor admitted to his office, greets him affably, offers him a seat, asks him whence he came and the nature of his business. The visitor sits down, touches briefly on his host's good fortune, stating he would be satisfied if he owned a half, a third of what Rothschild possessed. And he offers to sell the rich man one item he surely lacks: eternal life.

It goes without saying that when Rothschild hears the words eternal life, he pricks up his ears, asks for additional information and demands to know how much it would cost.

The Kasriel says three hundred, but Rothschild balks, saying it is too steep.

The Kasriel refuses to take less than three hundred.

Rothschild counts out the money. The visitor pockets it. To achieve eternal life, he tells Rothschild, he should leave Paris at once and come to Kasrilovka. Since Kasrilovka became a town, a rich man has never been known to die there.

Kasrilovka, Yehupetz and Boiberik, laughter-provoking names, became household words among Jews in Eastern Europe. In 1895, Tevyeh the Milkman made his initial appearance. One of Sholom Aleichem's major characters, Tevyeh was a hardworking man, a pauper, naturally, with a philosophical bent. He had an ailing wife, seven marriageable daughters and a horse that had known better days. Nothing ever went right with Tevyeh. His woes were as numerous as the days of the Jewish Exile. But the remarkable thing about Tevyeh was that after he was done complaining about his bitter fate, he went right on working, struggling and praying. A firm believer in God, Tevyeh had his own manner of communicating with Him. Sometimes he was not beyond chiding God.

Much as he suffered—one of his daughters married a Christian, another followed her husband, a revolutionist, to exile in Siberia—it never occurred to Tevyeh to admit defeat. The word "defeat" was as strange to him as the word "victory."

Now, the struggle for survival is not a subject for humorous sketches. They *can* be amusing, however, when written by a master like Sholom Aleichem. It wasn't Tevyeh's catalogue of disasters that made the readers laugh, but his reaction to them, his manner of coping with them.

13 Exile

Sholom Aleichem did not live to witness the massa-
cres at the end of World War I, when a quarter of a
million of his "little people" were slaughtered in the
Ukraine alone. He was dead almost a quarter of a
century when the Germans, under Hitler, killed six
million Jews. But he was in Kiev, in 1905, when
pogroms erupted all over the city and Jews were put
to the sword. Although he harbored no illusions
about the Czar and his attitude toward the Jews,
Sholom Aleichem would not have suspected that the
1905 revolution, which was suppressed, might be
used by the government as a pretext to kill Jews.
Pogroms started in the large cities, in Kishinev, in
Odessa and in Kiev. His beloved Kiev, the Yehupetz
of his stories, turned into a slaughterhouse.

He would not go on living in a land whose government condoned and encouraged the murder of Jews!

Sholom Aleichem went into exile.

The carriage was in front of the Sholom Aleichem house. The traveling bags had been loaded. The children had been seated. But the leave-taking was not over. Sholom Aleichem was shaking hands, embracing friends, kissing some. A few tears were inevitable. Surprisingly enough, there was laughter here and there, breaking through like the sun on a cloudy day. How many friends there were! He was poor in rubles but a Rothschild where friends were concerned.

"Goodbye."

"May you go in the best of health!"

"Come back to us soon!"

"Kiev will not be the same without you!"

Nor would he be the same—without Kiev. Leaving the city, the country, was not a decision he'd taken lightly. He was going away from his beloved "little people," the source of his lifeblood. A writer can remove himself from the well of his material and go on doing creative work. But Sholom Aleichem was at all times more than a writer. He was a partisan of his people's struggles, a voice of their inarticulate longings and desires, a singer of their hopes and aspirations. He was one with them.

From Russia Sholom Aleichem and his family went by train to Switzerland. Soon after their arrival he resumed work. To supplement his income he undertook a series of lectures in large Western European cities. Jews who knew Yiddish and many who did not, came to hear him read his stories and monologues. The crowds were responsive and applauded vigorously. But the difference between the receptions he received in the East and here were immediately apparent. Here, in the West, the audiences were, for the most part, polite. In Eastern Europe, on the other hand, the arrival of Sholom Aleichem was the occasion for a great outpouring of people. In Lemberg a large crowd greeted him at the railroad station. As the train carrying the illustrious visitor steamed into the station, the young people in the crowd set up a clamor. They carried Sholom Aleichem to the coach, unharnessed the horses and pulled the vehicle through the city streets.

Now thousands of West-European Jews became acquainted with the great Sholom Aleichem. Now they saw him with their eyes, the legend became a reality. They recognized his puckish face even before he was introduced. The merry twinkle was in his eye. He wore his hair long and was immaculately dressed in a velvet waistcoat. He had on a flowing tie and sparkling cufflinks.

After the tour he returned briefly to Switzerland. America was next on his itinerary. The halls were crowded. Unlike the other countries he had visited, America was not totally strange to him; many of his "little people" lived here. In the American cities he shook hands with thousands of his ex-Kasriels, took a penetrating look at how they lived and worked and spent their leisure time, and asked many questions. Not all the things he saw in America made him happy. True, his former "little people" no longer were hounded by a repressive government as they had been in Russia, they slept without fear of pogroms; but it seemed to him all their energies

were spent in "making a living," leaving hardly any
time for other things. The ex-Kasriels, whose numbers in America were legion, he found no longer
merry, although many of them were still poor. But
there were also a large number of *all-rightniks*
(well-to-do) and these went to the synagogue only
during the High Holy Days.

America proved a fascinating but also bewildering
experience. He returned to Europe in 1907, full of
new impressions and ideas for stories. He went
briefly to the Hague, capital city of Holland, as an
American delegate to the Zionist congress. There he
met the great Hebrew poet, Chaim Nachman Bialik,
who made his home in Odessa. The two embraced as
though they were old friends. So delighted were
they by the chance meeting, they spent most of their
time taking long walks, talking and laughing. Although Bialik wrote in Hebrew and Sholom Aleichem in Yiddish, there was a strong bond between
them, as both were attached to the traditional ways
of their people. Each recognized the other as a great
artist.

Sholom Aleichem returned to his family in Switzerland and there Bialik visited him. "Grandpa"
Mendele, an exile from Russia, like Sholom Aleichem, joined his friends. They sat in the shadow of
the massive Alps and talked for hours, about subjects dearest to their hearts, the Jewish people and
its literature. It goes without saying that "Grandpa" regaled them with stories. They pledged to meet
frequently and spoke hopefully of inducing Peretz to
come from Warsaw and join them; Peretz, that shin-

ing star in the Yiddish literary firmament who cast his glow far and wide. They planned optimistically for the future.

Even as his friends were getting ready to leave, Sholom Aleichem's mind was alive with plans for new stories. Why not write a children's book? He enjoyed writing for and about children. ''The Penknife,'' the story that brought him fame, was about a boy.

The children's world he knew, and would later write about, was for the most part a boy's world. It was a world filled with *don'ts*. A Jewish boy had his *rebbi's* whip to contend with or the dog belonging to a Christian neighbor. The heavy hand of punishment lurked everywhere, in *cheder,* in the home, in the woods, among Gentiles. But in spite of it all, Sholom Aleichem's youthful characters are filled with the tumult of life. Being Jewish, it appears, is no drawback at all, but a great gift from heaven.

Mottel Peissi, the cantor's boy, as Sholom Aleichem conceived him, was to be the most irrepressible of all his child characters. He would be Shmulik and Sholom and Meyer Medvedevker and Ali—he would encompass them all.

It was not long after that readers of Yiddish newspapers made their acquaintance with Mottel. Some compared Mottel to the American Tom Sawyer. Others argued that what happened to Mottel could happen only to a Jewish boy of a poor family, living in Kasrilovka. What is so ''adventurous,'' they asked, about having a father who is mortally ill? Mottel's father was on his deathbed. In the house there

wasn't money enough to buy the milk and bouillon
prescribed by the doctor. Many of the household
effects had been sold, among them the silver decant-
ers, prayer shawls, Mother's good dress and father's
books. Mottel was delighted by the rumpus, the hag-
gling and bargaining. But the sale of their cupboard
gave him special pleasure. How would they remove
this massive object from the house? The cupboard
had been with them so long it seemed to Mottel a
part of the wall. With the cupboard gone, he envi-
sioned certain problems for his mother, and this too
pleased him. Where would she lock the bread? Or
the matzohs, during Passover? Mottel was overjoyed
when someone bought his cot and the couch on
which his brother, Eli, slept. They would both sleep
on the floor!

When Mottel's father died, he could shout, hurrah, he was an orphan! He was excused from *cheder*
—a great event in itself—and was not compelled to
study. Moreover, everybody made a fuss over him,
offered him candy and sympathy. (Sholom Aleichem
well remembered the fuss made over him and the
other children after the death of his mother.) Mottel's neighbors felt sorry for him. But not the reader.
The reader laughs at Mottel's "adventures."

The author planned to write the Mottel book in
two parts, one dealing with the boy's life in Kasrilovka, the other with America. Now that Sholom
Aleichem had been to America, he must write about
the Jews who lived there. He conceived Mottel as a
bridge between Kasrilovka and America.

14 The anniversary

He was in his element, working, making notes, planning. At home there wasn't money enough for rent. His wallet was dry as a desert, he wrote to a close friend. Fortunately this was the year set aside by thousands of his readers throughout the world to celebrate his twenty-fifth anniversary as a writer. Men and women as poor as himself gave what little they could, pennies, mostly. The total sum that reached him was less than two hundred rubles. It was not enough, not nearly enough. But he was deeply moved by the gesture. He had sent out no alarm about the poverty in which he and his family lived. The world owed him nothing. He had always kept his sorrows to himself while giving the world laughter. He would go on as he had in the past. His health was not good. He was coughing a lot. Olga pleaded with him to go see a doctor.

He put her off with a smile. Who had time for a doctor? He had too much to do. The doctors took

your money. He did not have much of that to give.
What little money came in he wanted spent on the
family's needs.

But Olga persisted as his cough became worse.

He finally went. The doctor examined him thoroughly and diagnosed his ailment as tuberculosis.
Sholom Aleichem took the shocking news calmly.

He would have to rest, the doctor said, preferably
in a warm climate.

Out of the question, the sick man retorted. He
could not afford a warm climate; moreover, he had
too much to do.

But in the autumn of 1908 Sholom Aleichem went
with his family to Italy. However, instead of resting,
he was busy putting together a new book of stories.

Although he was well aware of his unhappy position, Sholom Aleichem would not disappoint his
readers by becoming solemn and serious. Always the
humorist, he maintained that there was no misfortune in the world that hasn't in it at least a germ of
good in it. God created leeches to attach themselves
to you and suck your blood while you're bathing, he
said. And yet, leeches were used for certain illnesses.
Bees sting, but they also supply honey. What
prompted him to mention these things in a foreword
to a book was that at one time he had been terribly
ill. He lay in bed in a small town near Kasrilovka,
spent two months there. But it was not the illness
that made him so unhappy at the time. It was his
doctor's strict order to avoid doing the following:
talk, read and write. One who understands what it is
for a drunk not to touch liquor can properly estimate

how he felt. They can forbid you to write, he mused
at the time, but can they keep you from thinking?
From his thoughts emerged characters and situa-
tions. A whole series of tales came to life in his mind.
These he took with him to Switzerland and now to
Italy where he completed the work.

Letters came from all parts of the world, urging
him to get well. Peretz wrote from Warsaw, admon-
ishing him to take care of himself, rise from the sickbed and return to his labors. "Your success is our
pride," Peretz declared.

The state of his health improved although he did
not fully recover. The Mottel episodes were increas-
ing in number. Mottel was now in America, a
"greenhorn." Mottel's older brother, Eli, found a
job and was "making a living." Sholom Aleichem
read the stories to his expanding family (two sons-
in-law having been added). They roared with delight
as Papa's impulse to mimic came to the fore. He
laughed along with the others until there were tears
in his eyes. He was happiest when in their midst,
reading to them, listening to their unrestrained
laughter, joining with them. This was a large audience he now had, for in addition to his own children
and sons-in-law, there were now two grandchildren.
Surrounded by his family, he found it possible, on
occasion, to forget one was in exile and ill. But there
wasn't any question about it, he would have to continue taking care of his health.

It was decided to go to a German summer resort.
Sholom Aleichem insisted the whole family go there.
He could not conceive parting with any of them.

The sons-in-law were like sons to him. He adored the two grandchildren. In the end, all of them went. Settled in Germany, he resumed his work. He looked forward to a fruitful summer. Money was trickling in, royalties from his stories, fees for occasional pieces he wrote for Yiddish newspapers. One son-in-law, I. D. Berkowitz, was translating the humorist's works into Hebrew. Sholom Aleichem was delighted. And indeed it appeared as though the master had a firm hold of the pen again, determined to complete what only the great French writer, Balzac, and to some extent Dickens, had done before him, to recreate through fiction a whole era, a history of his people. He would not let his illness stand in the way, or any other obstacle. What he did not count on was World War I, which burst upon an uneasy world, tearing to shreds many a noble plan.

Threatened by the Germans with internment as an enemy alien (he was a Russian citizen), Sholom Aleichem fled with his family to Denmark. Copenhagen, the Danish capital, was crowded with refugees. They found a place to live after much difficulty and he resumed his work. But the distant thunder of guns reached him in peaceful Copenhagen. He could not shut his ears to the anguished cry of humanity caught in the dreadful conflict. Nearest to his heart was the cry of his own people, the Jews, first victims in all conflicts. He knew from bitter experience, from reading of history, that no matter who won the war, the Jews would lose. How could he go on writing in the face of the universal insan-

ity? Work no longer came with ease. He felt ill. Olga prevailed upon him to go to the doctor.

"Diabetes," was the doctor's verdict. Sholom Aleichem was ordered to bed and was kept there by his family for seven weeks. Writing to a friend, he joked: "Having been told I have diabetes, I no longer fear dying of hunger. I'll most likely die of thirst."

In the United States word spread that Sholom Aleichem was bedridden in Copenhagen, without visible means of support. A Committee of One Hundred was formed, consisting of distinguished Yiddish writers, editors, artists, musicians, and even a few bankers. Money was collected to bring Sholom Aleichem and his family to America.

He arrived in the United States on December 3, 1914. All five Yiddish daily newspapers of New York printed banner headlines heralding his arrival. A welcoming committee met the incoming liner, which was late from dodging German mines and submarines in the Atlantic. At the pier there was a large crowd. There were flowers. Children from Hebrew schools sang songs and applauded. He descended on American soil—to stay.

15 The third-class passenger

The Hotel Theresa on 125th Street and Seventh Avenue, New York City, was a fashionable hostelry. Unfortunately, the rooms which the Committee of One Hundred were able to find for Sholom Aleichem were tiny. The occupants were cramped for space. Work was difficult. As Sholom Aleichem spoke no English—nor did any other member of the large family—they stayed at the hotel, waiting for rescue.

One day a young Columbia University student knocked on the door. He came in the hope of inducing the great humorist to address a Columbia class.

The visitor was shocked to find the room no larger than a "box." Sholom Aleichem, whom he recognized instantly, stood between bed and sofa, "as though he were at a railroad station, surrounded by his baggage." On his face now were deep traces of the storms he'd passed through. He greeted the young visitor warmly and inquired about the nature of his visit. The young man told him about the Columbia class and his own inspiring idea to invite the great humorist to address the group.

Sholom Aleichem listened attentively. He would gladly speak to the class, he said, if the young man would find him a place where he could prepare his talk. The visitor, whose name was B. Z. Goldberg, offered to help in any way possible.

He needed a place to live, Sholom Aleichem said.

The student offered to find a place.

The writer suggested his young visitor take along one of the daughters to help him search.

Not long after this chance encounter, Goldberg, aided by Sholom Aleichem's daughter (whom he later married), found an apartment for Sholom Aleichem on Lenox Avenue at 116th Street.

In the meantime, a meeting was arranged at Cooper Union. The hall filled early and hundreds of people were turned away at the door. The throng remained outside the hall, where Lincoln once spoke, hoping to catch a glimpse of the man whose laughter brightened their lives.

The guest of honor did not disappoint them. He entered the hall, mounted the rostrum and let his eyes roam over the sea of faces and began by telling them he'd come to America in 1905 for his first visit. This was his second one. On both occasions he came in the wake of a catastrophe. His first visit followed the bloody riots of 1905 in Russia. This time he was here because of the insanity, the war, in Europe. If ever it became necessary for him to come to America for a third time, he was hard put to it to imagine after what kind of catastrophe that would be. The worst, it seemed to him, had already happened.

After the Cooper Union meeting, there was Carnegie Hall. There, too, many were turned away from the doors of the packed hall.

Yiddish-speaking residents of New York came in large numbers of hear him speak and read from his works. People recognized him on the street and shook his hand and told him their troubles. He listened to what they said and how they said it. He tried to learn about them quickly in order to write about them. Soon he began writing stories and monologues about Jewish life in America. New Mottel episodes appeared. There was also his autobiography, which he could postpone no longer. But work did not come with ease. He no longer could ignore the fact that he was a sick man. Often, unable to rise, he wrote in bed.

He spent more and more time on his autobiography. His friends had insisted over a long period of time, he declared, that he tell the story of his life. He had made more than one attempt to carry out his friends' wishes. Several times he had sat down to work, but each time he let himself be diverted, until . . . until the right time came. Before reaching the age of fifty he had almost died. Now he would put it off no longer. No one knew what tomorrow might bring. One might die suddenly and people who thought they knew you and understood you would come up with peculiar stories about you. It was necessary to do the job yourself.

Unfortunately, he did not live to complete the work. But the episodes he committed to paper, sections of which are available in English as *The Great Fair,* translated by his granddaughter, Tamara Kahana, testify to the great loss suffered by world literature when Sholom Aleichem put down his pen for the last time.

He died on May 13, 1916, at the age of fifty-seven. Thirty thousand people escorted him to his final rest.

In his will, he cautioned his legatees to build no monuments in his memory, to make no glowing orations over his grave. He instructed them to bury him not among the rich and the eminent but among the working people and the common folk, that their graves may shine upon his and his upon theirs.

Who were these poor, the common folk? They were the vast majority of Jews crowding the slums of the East Side of New York, the West Side of Chicago and all other ghettos of the great cities of America where the ''little people'' lived. From these people, who had nothing save their faith and a stubborn will to survive, he had drawn his creative lifeblood. Even during his brief period of wealth he maintained his bond with them.

During the lifetime of a writer, an artist or a composer, there arise honest differences of opinion among critics as to whether the person's work is the kind that enjoys temporary popularity or whether it will endure. Time passes its own judgment. Sholom

Aleichem survives. The world about which he wrote is dead, but he survives. In 1959, one hundred years after his birth, celebrations were held throughout the world to commemorate the man and his work. In the United States, exhibitions of Sholom Aleichem's works were held in many libraries, and in meeting halls his stories were read. The Russian and Israeli governments issued commemorative stamps in his honor.

He is read in a good many of the languages devised by man. He has taken his place among the immortals.

Some books in English by and about Sholom Aleichem: *The Old Country*, translated by Julius and Frances Butwin. *The Adventures of Mottel, The Great Fair*, both translated by Tamara Kahana. *The World of Sholom Aleichem*, by Maurice Samuel, an original work dealing with the man, his work and the time about which he wrote. *Wandering Star*, translated by Frances Butwin. *Selected Stories of Sholom Aleichem*, introduction by Alfred Kazin. *My Father Sholom Aleichem* by Marie Waife-Goldberg.